FAMOUS FOR A DAY

SING IN YOUR FAV BAND

4.0 GPA Forever

1000 More Coke or Pepsi questions 2 ask your friends!

THINK U AND YOUR FRIENDS HAVE A LOT IN COMMON?

FINE print
PUBLISHING

Written and designed by
Mickey & Cheryl Gill

FINE print
P U B L I S H I N G

Fine Print Publishing Company
P.O. Box 916401
Longwood, Florida 32971-6401

ISBN 1-892951-40-1

coke-or-pepsi.com

**PASS THIS BOOK ON TO ALL YOUR FRIENDS.
EACH ONE GETS TO ANSWER CRAZY COOL QUESTIONS.**

**SOUL-SEARCHING AND SOMETIMES
SILLY QUESTIONS REVEAL
WHAT YOUR FRIENDS
ARE MADE OF!**

**ANSWER A SET
OF QUESTIONS
AND PASS IT
BACK.**

Do U wear your friends' clothes?
○ YES ○ NO

Love is ○ wonderful ○ cruel ○ complicated

R U SQUEAMISH? ○ Yes ○ No

coke-or-pepsi
.com

If U could invent something,
what would it B?
time machine

1. My name is _____

2. I wish my name were _____

3. Ever been embarrassed by parents? ◯ Yes ◯ No

4. Any details 4 #3? _____

5. What famous person would you trade places with? _____

6. If you could invent something, what would it be? _____

7. How many teeth do you have? _____

8. Whiten your teeth? ◯ Yes, over-the-counter ◯ Yes, professionally ◯ No

9. How many times a day do you brush your teeth? _____

10. Rules should be ◯ followed ◯ used as guidelines ◯ broken

11. Worst fashion mistake you've ever made? _____

12. Most annoying thing about school? _____

13. Best thing about school? _____

14. Do you exercise? ◯ Yes ◯ No ◯ Sometimes

15. If yes to #14, what kind? _____

16. Most outrageous thing you've ever eaten? _____

17. ◯ Pay now, play later ◯ Play now, pay later?

18. Little kids are ◯ fun ◯ annoying?

19. Write papers ◯ in advance ◯ a few days before ◯ night before?

20. Study ◯ alone ◯ with a friend ◯ in a group?

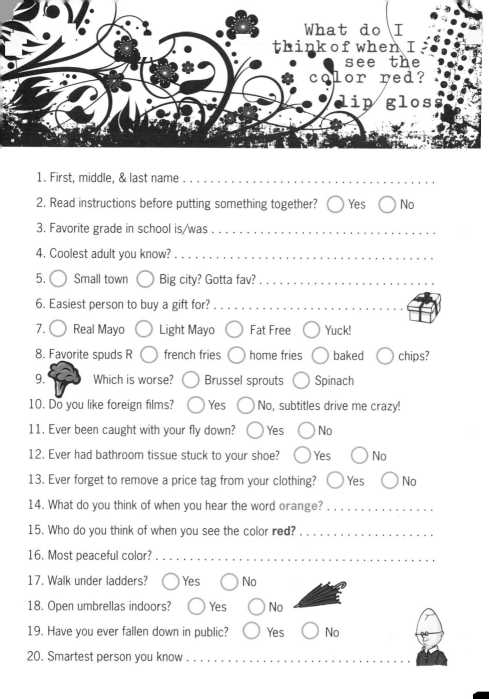

What do I think of when I see the color red?

lip gloss

1. First, middle, & last name . . . .

2. Read instructions before putting something together? ( ) Yes ( ) No

3. Favorite grade in school is/was . . . .

4. Coolest adult you know? . . . .

5. ( ) Small town ( ) Big city? Gotta fav? . . . .

6. Easiest person to buy a gift for? . . . .

7. ( ) Real Mayo ( ) Light Mayo ( ) Fat Free ( ) Yuck!

8. Favorite spuds R ( ) french fries ( ) home fries ( ) baked ( ) chips?

9. Which is worse? ( ) Brussel sprouts ( ) Spinach

10. Do you like foreign films? ( ) Yes ( ) No, subtitles drive me crazy!

11. Ever been caught with your fly down? ( ) Yes ( ) No

12. Ever had bathroom tissue stuck to your shoe? ( ) Yes ( ) No

13. Ever forget to remove a price tag from your clothing? ( ) Yes ( ) No

14. What do you think of when you hear the word orange? . . . .

15. Who do you think of when you see the color red? . . . .

16. Most peaceful color? . . . .

17. Walk under ladders? ( ) Yes ( ) No

18. Open umbrellas indoors? ( ) Yes ( ) No

19. Have you ever fallen down in public? ( ) Yes ( ) No

20. Smartest person you know . . . .

1. Your name please _____

2. Last time you read a newspaper? _____

3. Last time you opened a dictionary? _____

4. Last thing you cooked? _____

5. Favorite room in the house/apartment? _____

6. Favorite decorating style? _____

7. Describe your style of dressing _____

8. R U having a ◯ good hair day ◯ bad hair day ◯ so-so hair day?

9. Do you wear your friends' clothes? ◯ Yes ◯ No

10. Who encourages you the most? _____

11. Can you name all of Santa's reindeer? ◯ Yes ◯ No

12. Did you say yes? Go ahead then. _____

13. Do you like egg nog? ◯ Yes ◯ No

14. Favorite holiday treat? _____

15. R U squeamish? ◯ Yes ◯ No

16. If yes, what makes you squeamish? _____

17. R U an adventurous eater? _____

18. Camping: ◯ tent ◯ cabin ◯ RV

19. Ever encounter a wild animal? ◯ Yes, what? _____ ◯ No

20. Favorite amusement park? _____

Best personality trait?
Loyalty

1. My initials are _____

2. Favorite kind of dog? _____

3. Your worst personality trait? _____

4. Your best personality trait? _____

5. I know a lot about _____

6. I know absolutely nothing about _____

7. Holidays are ◯ fun with my family ◯ a nightmare with my family

8. Most embarrassing moment ever was _____

9. What have U dreamed of doing, but think U can't? _____

10. Why? _____

11. Any new goals? ◯ Yes, what? _____ ◯ No

12. Ever reached a goal? ◯ Yes, what? _____ ◯ No

13. ◯ I love waking up to birds ◯ I hate birds waking me up

14. Bedtime rituals? ◯ Yes, what?_____ ◯ No

15. Morning rituals? ◯ Yes, what?_____ ◯ No

16. R U a sucker for a happy ending? ◯ Yes ◯ No

17. Who taught you how to tie your shoes? _____

18. Do you know who your Dad's hero is? ◯ Yes, who_____ ◯ No

19. How about your Mom's? ◯ Yes, who_____ ◯ No

20. Who's your hero? _____

What kind of fries do I like?
It doesn't matter as long as I have ketchup.

★ ★ ★ ★ ★

1. My name is . . . .

2. Do you believe in magic? ◯ Yes ◯ No

3. Worst thing U have ever eaten? . . . .

4. Movie U can watch over and over? . . . .

5. Worst show on T.V. right now? . . . .

6. Ever pretend to love a gift that you really hated? ◯ Yes ◯ No

7. French fries: ◯ thin ◯ crinkle cut ◯ steak ◯ waffle?

8. Bagel: ◯ plain ◯ whole wheat ◯ sweet ◯ everything?

9. More about your bagel: ◯ naked ◯ cream cheese?

10. ◯ Board games ◯ Bored with games?

11. If safety weren't a problem, what animal would U have as a pet? . . . .

12. Favorite number? . . . .

13. Best advice anyone ever gave you? . . . .

14. Worst advice anyone ever gave you? . . . .

15. Ever stay up all night watching movies? ◯ Yes ◯ No

16. Ever stay up all night talking to a friend on the phone? ◯ Yes ◯ No

17. Do you order stuff on the Internet? ◯ Yes ◯ No

18. What "super sense" would U like? ◯ Hearing ◯ Sight ◯ Smell

19. What fashion item defines you? . . . .

20. Like what you are wearing right now? ◯ Yes ◯ No

1. My friends call me _____
   (name)

2. I get my music from ◯ the store ◯ online ◯ both

3. Describe your BF in 1 word _____

4. Ever want to be a d.j. on the radio? ◯ Yes ◯ No

5. If yes, what music would you play? _____

6. 🍀 Do U wear green on St. Patrick's Day? ◯ Yes ◯ No

7. Do U miss kid stuff like hunting Easter eggs? ◯ Yes ◯ No

8. How about putting your tooth under your pillow? ◯ Yes ◯ No

9. Do you know what T.T.F.N. stands 4? ◯ Yes, what? _____ ◯ No

10. How do U get a song out of your head? _____

11. What do U splurge on? _____

12. Which describes you best? ◯ Emotional ◯ Logical ◯ 50/50

13. R U ◯ extroverted ◯ introverted ◯ somewhere in the middle?

14. I prefer a ◯ picnic in the park ◯ great night out

15. Most boring sport to watch? _____

16. What celebrity your BFF would identify U with? _____

17. Ever had a premonition? ◯ Yes ◯ No

18. How would your parents describe you? _____

19. U find $50. You ◯ bank it ◯ spend it ◯ try to find its owner

20. What did you watch on TV last night? _____

Robot?

I think I'll have one to do the things I hate!

1. The name I was born with is . . . .

2. How would U spend $1000 in 1 day? . . . .

3. What have you planned that became a disaster? . . . .

4. Do U have a profle on MYSPACE? ◯ Yes ◯ No

5. Favorite book character? . . . .

6. Best band since you were born? . . . .

7. I lose track of time when I . . . .

8. Do you think you will own a robot in the future? ◯ Yes ◯ No

9. Your friends come to U when they need a ◯ pep talk ◯ reality check

10. What do U do in your spare time? . . . .

11. Do you talk 2 your pet like it's a person? ◯ Yes ◯ No

12. ◯ Spend more time dwelling on the past ◯ Looking toward the future?

13. How long do you think civilization will last? . . . .

14. Lesson you've learned the hard way? . . . .

15. Where R U right now? . . . .

16. Who are U sitting next 2 right now? . . . .

17. How many times do you hit Snooze? . . . .

18. What do U think happens to your soul when you die? . . . .

19. ◯ Can U Yo-Yo? ◯ Yes ◯ No ◯ Who cares

20. Do U like being in the spotlight? ◯ Always ◯ Sometimes ◯ Never

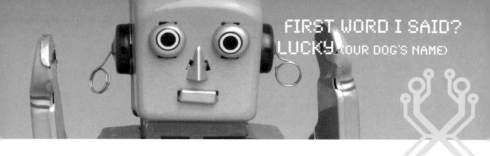

1. Name on your birth certificate? _____

2. Day of the week, date, and time of your birth? _____

3. First word you said? _____

4. Most beautiful sounding language? _____

5. Feel like you're in control of your life? ◯ Yes ◯ No

6. Do U read the label on food before U buy? ◯ Yes ◯ No

7. Who do you trust with the deep stuff? _____

8. When U R mad, do U ◯ yell ◯ cry ◯ get quiet?

9. Best memory U have? _____

10. Worst memory U have? _____

11. ◯ Make quick decisions ◯ Think about it ◯ Avoid making decisions?

12. Any regrets? ◯ Yes, what?_____ ◯ No

13. If U had an extra hour every day, what would U do? _____

14. Describe a typical Saturday a.m. _____

15. Ever flown in a helicopter? ◯ Yes ◯ No

16. Something most people don't know about U? _____

17. ◯ Green thumb ◯ Kill everything ◯ Never tried to grow anything?

18. ◯ Daisies ◯ Roses ◯ Other _____ ?

19. Which is worse? ◯ Paper cut ◯ Burning your tongue?

20. I'm like ◯ my mom ◯ my dad ◯ neither — I might be an alien!

1. List all the names you go by _____

2. One word to describe you? _____

3. ◯ Unicorn   ◯ Pegasus   ◯ Dragon   ◯ Other _____

4. Ever rode on the handlebars of a bike?   ◯ Yes   ◯ No

5. What's outside your window right now? _____

6. What kind of student R U?   ◯ Great   ◯ So-so   ◯ Not-so-good

7. Who makes you laugh the hardest? _____

8. Who is your favorite superhero? _____

9. What would U like to be remembered 4? _____

10. Ever had surgery?   ◯ Yes, what kind? _____   ◯ No

11. Favorite movie song? _____

12. What's something that amazes U? _____

13. What do U sweeten with? ◯ Pink stuff ◯ Blue stuff ◯ Yellow stuff ◯ Real stuff

14. Read anything good lately?   ◯ Yes, what? _____   ◯ No

15. Can you whistle a tune?   ◯ Of course   ◯ A little bit   ◯ No

16. One word to describe girls? _____

17. One word to describe boys? _____

18. Mountains: ◯ s'mores next to the fire ◯ climbing rocks ◯ hiking on trails?

19. Something legal U R addicted to? _____

20. Weirdest movie you've ever seen? _____

What word do I always misspell?

Necessary

1. Last name?. . . . .

2. What do U want to B when U grow up? . . . .

3. Ever enter a competition? ◯ Yes, what? . . . . ◯ No

4. Did you win? ◯ Yes, what? . . . . ◯ Nah

5. What's your typical Sunday morning? . . . .

6. What's something U R proud of? . . . .

7. What word do U always mispell? . . . .

8. Scared of heights? ◯ Yes ◯ No

9. Favorite chewing gum or mint? . . . .

10. Can you use chopsticks? ◯ Yes ◯ No

11. What perfume/cologne do you wear? . . . .

12. ◯ Chocolate cake with chocolate icing ◯ Angel food cake with fruit?

13. ◯ Pencil ◯ Mechanical pencil ◯ Ballpoint ◯ Gel pen?

14. Which is worse? ◯ Headache ◯ Toothache ◯ Stomachache ◯ Backache

15. ◯ 4.0 GPA for a year ◯ Spending time with your crush for a year

16. What piece(s) of jewelry do U always wear? . . . .

17. What do you love about summer? . . . .

18. ◯ Green tea ◯ Hot tea ◯ Iced tea ◯ Tea cookies?

19. Ever baked a cake? ◯ Yes ◯ No

20. Do you believe in ◯ fate ◯ God ◯ yourself?

FAVORITE
FROZEN
TREAT?

ORANGE
POPSICLE

1. First name? ◯ Yes, what is it? . . . . ◯ No

2. If U could only go to 1 concert this year, who would U see? . . . . . .

3. Describe the watch you're wearing. . . . .

4. Rank in order of liking: ___ Eagle ___ Horse ___ Cheetah ___ Dolphin ___ Pig

5. 😄 R U good at telling jokes? ◯ Yes ◯ No

6. Think life is ◯ fair ◯ unfair ◯ what you make it?

7. Which would U play? ◯ Damsel in distress ◯ Superhero ◯ Super villain?

8. What's your biggest question about life? . . . .

9. Ever in a school play? ◯ Yes, who/what were you? . . . . ◯ No

10. Do U listen to ◯ the words in music ◯ just the music?

11. Have a fav cartoon? ◯ Yes, what? . . . . ◯ No, don't watch anymore

12. What's cutest? ◯ Puppies ◯ Kittens ◯ Other . . . .

13. Favorite character from an animated movie? . . . .

14. Weirdest animal you've ever seen? . . . .

15. ◯ Aqua ◯ Fuchsia ◯ Mint ◯ Black ◯ Cream ◯ Violet

16. Favorite clothing brand? . . . .

17. Favorite cold beverage? . . . .

18. Your friends would describe U as ◯ sweet ◯ reliable ◯ crazy

19. Favorite frozen treat? . . . .

20. What would you like to be doing 10 years from now? . . . .

Pet trick?
My cat fetches.

1. Name _____ I wish it were _____

2. Do U feel sorry 4 the bad singers on American Idol? ◯ Yes ◯ No

3. When U talk on the phone do U: ◯ pace ◯ use hand gestures ◯ both?

4. Do you laugh when you hit your funny bone? ◯ Yes ◯ No

5. Vacation time! ◯ Big city ◯ Warm beach ◯ Another country

6. Do you like to read poetry? ◯ Yes ◯ Not really

7. R U known 4 your ◯ sense of humor ◯ good taste ◯ talent?

8. What duo R U & your bff most like? ◯ Batman & Robin ◯ Scooby & Shaggy

9. You love ◯ a little make-up ◯ a lot of make-up

10. R U ◯ Miss Adventure ◯ Miss Understood ◯ Miss Informed?

11. Favorite vegetable? _____

12. ◯ Fast food ◯ Themed restaurant ◯ Fine dining?

13. What do U do when you can't sleep? _____

14. Your dream machine is ◯ biggest SUV ◯ smallest sports car ◯ limo

15. ◯ Mac ◯ PC

16. Ever been a member of a fan club? ◯ Yes, which one? _____ ◯ No

17. Do U have a celebrity autograph? ◯ Yes, who? _____ ◯ No

18. Do U tell people when they have food stuck in their teeth? ◯ Yes ◯ No

19. Have a pet that does a cool trick? ◯ Yes, what? _____ ◯ No

20. Favorite thing hanging on your room wall? _____

FAVORITE JUNK FOOD?
TWINKIES

1. Name? _____

2. ◯ Thick   ◯ Thin   ◯ Sicilian   ◯ Stuffed?

3. What do U like in your H20?   ◯ Lemon   ◯ Lime   ◯ Nothing

4. Ever been on television?   ◯ Yes, why? _____ ◯ No

5. Who has it easier?   ◯ Girls   ◯ Boys

6. Chips: ◯ Sour cream/onion   ◯ Barbeque   ◯ Cheddar   ◯ Plain?

7. Favorite flavor of jelly, jam or preserves?_____

8. In a long line, do U ◯ look at your watch ◯ mumble aloud ◯ wait patiently?

9. ◯ Banana   ◯ Banana nut bread   ◯ Banana cream pie?

10. Is it hard for you to say U R sorry?   ◯ Yes   ◯ No

11. ◯ Scrambled   ◯ Fried   ◯ Poached   ◯ Hard-boiled   ◯ None?

12. Most boring book you've ever read?_____

13. Favorite kind of meat?_____

14. Fav movie food? ◯ Popcorn ◯ Twizzlers ◯ Nachos ◯ Other _____?

15. What TV show would you like to star in?_____

16. What's something you love that most people hate? _____

17. Ever think U R crazy? ◯ All the time ◯ Sometimes ◯ No, everyone else is!

18. Favorite junk food?_____

19. Do you take naps?   ◯ Yes   ◯ No

20. ◯ Original   ◯ Extra crispy   ◯ Spicy?

Word I don't like?

blood.

1. First name spelled backwards? . . . .
2. Last movie U saw? . . . .
3. ⃝ Taco   ⃝ Burrito   ⃝ Enchilada   ⃝ Fajita?
4. What's your ring tone on your cell phone? . . . .
5. What's the most popular color in your wardrobe? . . . .
6. Coolest Arctic animal? ⃝ Penguin ⃝ Polar bear ⃝ Harp seal ⃝ Killer whale
7. R U usually ⃝ too hot   ⃝ too cold?
8. R U allergic to anything? ⃝ Yes, what? . . . .   ⃝ No
9. Favorite CD at the moment? . . . .
10. Is it hard for U to say U R wrong? ⃝ Yes   ⃝ No
11. Favorite TV actor? . . . .
12. Favorite TV actress? . . . .
13. Least favorite class in school? . . . .
14. Ever entered through a "Do Not Enter" door? ⃝ Yes ⃝ No
15. What's a word you don't like? . . . .
16. How did U meet your BF? . . . .
17. What celebrity would U not trade places with? . . . .
18. Do you study ⃝ in a quiet room   ⃝ with music on   ⃝ with TV on?
19. How many pairs of shoes do U own? ⃝ 10 or fewer ⃝ 10-20 ⃝ 20 plus
20. Favorite sandwich? . . . .

1. My name is _____

2. I wish my name were _____

3. Ever been embarrassed by parents? ◯ Yes ◯ No

4. Any details 4 #3? _____

5. What famous person would you trade places with? _____

6. If you could invent something, what would it be? _____

7. How many teeth do you have? _____

8. Whiten your teeth? ◯ Yes, over-the-counter ◯ Yes, professionally ◯ No

9. How many times a day do you brush your teeth? _____

10. Rules should be ◯ followed ◯ used as guidelines ◯ broken

11. Worst fashion mistake you've ever made? _____

12. Most annoying thing about school? _____

13. Best thing about school? _____

14. Do you exercise? ◯ Yes ◯ No ◯ Sometimes

15. If yes to #14, what kind? _____

16. Most outrageous thing you've ever eaten? _____

17. ◯ Pay now, play later ◯ Play now, pay later?

18. Little kids are ◯ fun ◯ annoying?

19. Write papers ◯ in advance ◯ a few days before ◯ night before?

20. Study ◯ alone ◯ with a friend ◯ in a group?

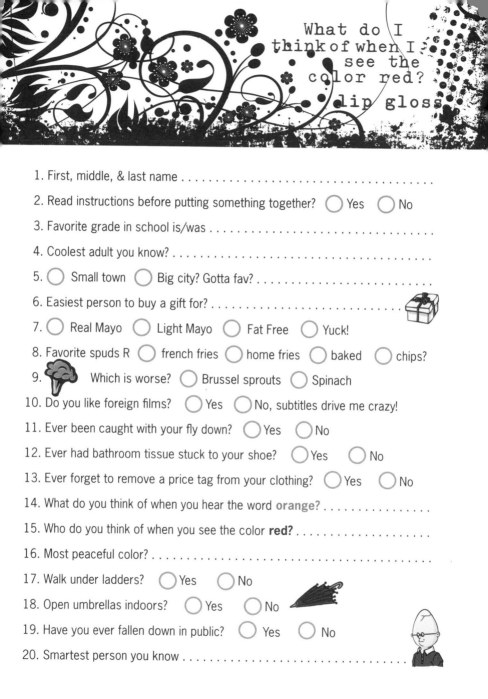

What do I think of when I see the color red?

lip gloss

1. First, middle, & last name . . . .

2. Read instructions before putting something together? ◯ Yes ◯ No

3. Favorite grade in school is/was . . . .

4. Coolest adult you know? . . . .

5. ◯ Small town ◯ Big city? Gotta fav? . . . .

6. Easiest person to buy a gift for? . . . .

7. ◯ Real Mayo ◯ Light Mayo ◯ Fat Free ◯ Yuck!

8. Favorite spuds R ◯ french fries ◯ home fries ◯ baked ◯ chips?

9. Which is worse? ◯ Brussel sprouts ◯ Spinach

10. Do you like foreign films? ◯ Yes ◯ No, subtitles drive me crazy!

11. Ever been caught with your fly down? ◯ Yes ◯ No

12. Ever had bathroom tissue stuck to your shoe? ◯ Yes ◯ No

13. Ever forget to remove a price tag from your clothing? ◯ Yes ◯ No

14. What do you think of when you hear the word **orange?** . . . .

15. Who do you think of when you see the color **red?** . . . .

16. Most peaceful color? . . . .

17. Walk under ladders? ◯ Yes ◯ No

18. Open umbrellas indoors? ◯ Yes ◯ No

19. Have you ever fallen down in public? ◯ Yes ◯ No

20. Smartest person you know . . . .

1. Your name please _____

2. Last time you read a newspaper? _____

3. Last time you opened a dictionary? _____

4. Last thing you cooked? _____

5. Favorite room in the house/apartment? _____

6. Favorite decorating style? _____

7. Describe your style of dressing _____

8. R U having a ◯ good hair day ◯ bad hair day ◯ so-so hair day?

9. Do you wear your friends' clothes? ◯ Yes ◯ No

10. Who encourages you the most? _____

11. Can you name all of Santa's reindeer? ◯ Yes ◯ No

12. Did you say yes? Go ahead then. _____

13. Do you like egg nog? ◯ Yes ◯ No

14. Favorite holiday treat? _____

15. R U squeamish? ◯ Yes ◯ No

16. If yes, what makes you squeamish? _____

17. R U an adventurous eater? _____

18. Camping: ◯ tent ◯ cabin ◯ RV

19. Ever encounter a wild animal? ◯ Yes, what? _____ ◯ No

20. Favorite amusement park? _____

Best personality trait?
Loyalty

1. My initials are _____

2. Favorite kind of dog? _____

3. Your worst personality trait? _____

4. Your best personality trait? _____

5. I know a lot about _____

6. I know absolutely nothing about _____

7. Holidays are ◯ fun with my family ◯ a nightmare with my family

8. Most embarrassing moment ever was _____

9. What have U dreamed of doing, but think U can't? _____

10. Why? _____

11. Any new goals? ◯ Yes, what? _____ ◯ No

12. Ever reached a goal? ◯ Yes, what? _____ ◯ No

13. ◯ I love waking up to birds ◯ I hate birds waking me up

14. Bedtime rituals? ◯ Yes, what?_____ ◯ No

15. Morning rituals? ◯ Yes, what?_____ ◯ No

16. R U a sucker for a happy ending? ◯ Yes ◯ No

17. Who taught you how to tie your shoes? _____

18. Do you know who your Dad's hero is? ◯ Yes, who_____ ◯ No

19. How about your Mom's? ◯ Yes, who_____ ◯ No

20. Who's your hero? _____

What kind of fries do I like?
It doesn't matter as long as I have ketchup.

★ ★ ★ ★ ★

1. My name is . . . .

2. Do you believe in magic? ◯ Yes ◯ No

3. Worst thing U have ever eaten? . . . .

4. Movie U can watch over and over? . . . .

5. Worst show on T.V. right now? . . . .

6. Ever pretend to love a gift that you really hated? ◯ Yes ◯ No

7. French fries: ◯ thin ◯ crinkle cut ◯ steak ◯ waffle?

8. Bagel: ◯ plain ◯ whole wheat ◯ sweet ◯ everything?

9. More about your bagel: ◯ naked ◯ cream cheese?

10. ◯ Board games ◯ Bored with games?

11. If safety weren't a problem, what animal would U have as a pet? . . . .

12. Favorite number? . . . .

13. Best advice anyone ever gave you? . . . .

14. Worst advice anyone ever gave you? . . . .

15. Ever stay up all night watching movies? ◯ Yes ◯ No

16. Ever stay up all night talking to a friend on the phone? ◯ Yes ◯ No

17. Do you order stuff on the Internet? ◯ Yes ◯ No

18. What "super sense" would U like? ◯ Hearing ◯ Sight ◯ Smell

19. What fashion item defines you? . . . .

20. Like what you are wearing right now? ◯ Yes ◯ No

1. My friends call me _____
   (name)

2. I get my music from ⚪ the store ⚪ online ⚪ both

3. Describe your BF in 1 word _____

4. Ever want to be a d.j. on the radio? ⚪ Yes ⚪ No

5. If yes, what music would you play? _____

6. Do U wear green on St. Patrick's Day? ⚪ Yes ⚪ No

7. Do U miss kid stuff like hunting Easter eggs? ⚪ Yes ⚪ No

8. How about putting your tooth under your pillow? ⚪ Yes ⚪ No

9. Do you know what T.T.F.N. stands 4? ⚪ Yes, what? _____ ⚪ No

10. How do U get a song out of your head? _____

11. What do U splurge on? _____

12. Which describes you best? ⚪ Emotional ⚪ Logical ⚪ 50/50

13. R U ⚪ extroverted ⚪ introverted ⚪ somewhere in the middle?

14. I prefer a ⚪ picnic in the park ⚪ great night out

15. Most boring sport to watch? _____

16. What celebrity your BFF would identify U with? _____

17. Ever had a premonition? ⚪ Yes ⚪ No

18. How would your parents describe you? _____

19. U find $50. You ⚪ bank it ⚪ spend it ⚪ try to find its owner

20. What did you watch on TV last night? _____

Robot?
I think I'll have one to do the things I hate!

1. The name I was born with is . . . .

2. How would U spend $1000 in 1 day? . . . .

3. What have you planned that became a disaster? . . . .

4. Do U have a profle on MYSPACE? ◯ Yes ◯ No

5. Favorite book character? . . . .

6. Best band since you were born? . . . .

7. I lose track of time when I . . . .

8. Do you think you will own a robot in the future? ◯ Yes ◯ No

9. Your friends come to U when they need a ◯ pep talk ◯ reality check

10. What do U do in your spare time? . . . .

11. Do you talk 2 your pet like it's a person? ◯ Yes ◯ No

12. ◯ Spend more time dwelling on the past ◯ Looking toward the future?

13. How long do you think civilization will last? . . . .

14. Lesson you've learned the hard way? . . . .

15. Where R U right now? . . . .

16. Who are U sitting next 2 right now? . . . .

17. How many times do you hit Snooze? . . . .

18. What do U think happens to your soul when you die? . . . .

19. ◯ Can U Yo-Yo? ◯ Yes ◯ No ◯ Who cares

20. Do U like being in the spotlight? ◯ Always ◯ Sometimes ◯ Never

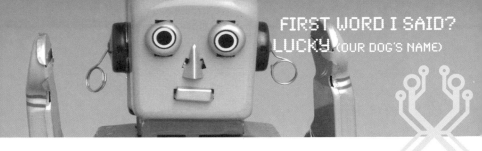

1. Name on your birth certificate? _____

2. Day of the week, date, and time of your birth? _____

3. First word you said? _____

4. Most beautiful sounding language? _____

5. Feel like you're in control of your life? ◯ Yes ◯ No

6. Do U read the label on food before U buy? ◯ Yes ◯ No

7. Who do you trust with the deep stuff? _____

8. When U R mad, do U ◯ yell ◯ cry ◯ get quiet?

9. Best memory U have? _____

10. Worst memory U have? _____

11. ◯ Make quick decisions ◯ Think about it ◯ Avoid making decisions?

12. Any regrets? ◯ Yes, what?_____ ◯ No

13. If U had an extra hour every day, what would U do? _____

14. Describe a typical Saturday a.m. _____

15. Ever flown in a helicopter? ◯ Yes ◯ No

16. Something most people don't know about U? _____

17. ◯ Green thumb ◯ Kill everything ◯ Never tried to grow anything?

18. ◯ Daisies ◯ Roses ◯ Other _____?

19. Which is worse? ◯ Paper cut ◯ Burning your tongue?

20. I'm like ◯ my mom ◯ my dad ◯ neither — I might be an alien!

1. List all the names you go by _____

2. One word to describe you? _____

3. ◯ Unicorn ◯ Pegasus ◯ Dragon ◯ Other _____

4. Ever rode on the handlebars of a bike? ◯ Yes ◯ No

5. What's outside your window right now? _____

6. What kind of student R U? ◯ Great ◯ So-so ◯ Not-so-good

7. Who makes you laugh the hardest? _____

8. Who is your favorite superhero? _____

9. What would U like to be remembered 4? _____

10. Ever had surgery? ◯ Yes, what? _____ ◯ No

11. Favorite movie song? _____

12. What's something that amazes U? _____

13. What do U sweeten with? ◯ Pink stuff ◯ Blue stuff ◯ Yellow stuff ◯ Real stuff

14. Read anything good lately? ◯ Yes, what? _____ ◯ No

15. Can you whistle a tune? ◯ Of course ◯ A little bit ◯ No

16. One word to describe girls? _____

17. One word to describe boys? _____

18. Mountains: ◯ s'mores next to the fire ◯ climbing rocks ◯ hiking on trails?

19. Something legal U R addicted to? _____

20. Weirdest movie you've ever seen? _____

What word do I always misspell?

Necessary

1. Last name?. . . . .

2. What do U want to B when U grow up? . . . .

3. Ever enter a competition? ◯ Yes, what? . . . . ◯ No

4. Did you win? ◯ Yes, what? . . . . ◯ Nah

5. What's your typical Sunday morning? . . . .

6. What's something U R proud of? . . . .

7. What word do U always misspell? . . . .

8. Scared of heights? ◯ Yes ◯ No

9. Favorite chewing gum or mint? . . . .

10. Can you use chopsticks? ◯ Yes ◯ No

11. What perfume/cologne do you wear? . . . .

12. ◯ Chocolate cake with chocolate icing ◯ Angel food cake with fruit?

13. ◯ Pencil ◯ Mechanical pencil ◯ Ballpoint ◯ Gel pen?

14. Which is worse? ◯ Headache ◯ Toothache ◯ Stomachache ◯ Backache

15. ◯ 4.0 GPA for a year ◯ Spending time with your crush for a year

16. What piece(s) of jewelry do U always wear? . . . .

17. What do you love about summer? . . . .

18. ◯ Green tea ◯ Hot tea ◯ Iced tea ◯ Tea cookies?

19. Ever baked a cake? ◯ Yes ◯ No

20. Do you believe in ◯ fate ◯ God ◯ yourself?

1. First name? ◯ Yes, what is it? . . . . ◯ No

2. If U could only go to 1 concert this year, who would U see? . . . .

3. Describe the watch you're wearing. . . . .

4. Rank in order of liking: __ Eagle __ Horse __ Cheetah __ Dolphin __ Pig

5. 😄 R U good at telling jokes? ◯ Yes ◯ No

6. Think life is ◯ fair ◯ unfair ◯ what you make it?

7. Which would U play? ◯ Damsel in distress ◯ Superhero ◯ Super villain?

8. What's your biggest question about life? . . . .

9. Ever in a school play? ◯ Yes, who/what were you? . . . . ◯ No

10. Do U listen to ◯ the words in music ◯ just the music?

11. Have a fav cartoon? ◯ Yes, what? . . . . ◯ No, don't watch anymore

12. What's cutest? ◯ Puppies ◯ Kittens ◯ Other . . . .

13. Favorite character from an animated movie? . . . .

14. Weirdest animal you've ever seen? . . . .

15. ◯ Aqua ◯ Fuchsia ◯ Mint ◯ Black ◯ Cream ◯ Violet

16. Favorite clothing brand? . . . .

17. Favorite cold beverage? 🥤 . . . .

18. Your friends would describe U as ◯ sweet ◯ reliable ◯ crazy

19. Favorite frozen treat? . . . .

20. What would you like to be doing 10 years from now? . . . .

Pet trick?
My cat fetches.

1. Name _____ I wish it were _____

2. Do U feel sorry 4 the bad singers on American Idol? ◯ Yes ◯ No

3. When U talk on the phone do U: ◯ pace ◯ use hand gestures ◯ both?

4. ⚡ Do you laugh when you hit your funny bone? ◯ Yes ◯ No

5. Vacation time! ◯ Big city ◯ Warm beach ◯ Another country

6. Do you like to read poetry? ◯ Yes ◯ Not really

7. R U known 4 your ◯ sense of humor ◯ good taste ◯ talent?

8. What duo R U & your bff most like? ◯ Batman & Robin ◯ Scooby & Shaggy

9. You love ◯ a little make-up ◯ a lot of make-up

10. R U ◯ Miss Adventure ◯ Miss Understood ◯ Miss Informed?

11. Favorite vegetable? _____

12. ◯ Fast food ◯ Themed restaurant ◯ Fine dining?

13. What do U do when you can't sleep? _____

14. Your dream machine is ◯ biggest SUV ◯ smallest sports car ◯ limo

15. ◯ Mac ◯ PC

16. Ever been a member of a fan club? ◯ Yes, which one? _____ ◯ No

17. Do U have a celebrity autograph? ◯ Yes, who? _____ ◯ No

18. Do U tell people when they have food stuck in their teeth? ◯ Yes ◯ No

19. Have a pet that does a cool trick? ◯ Yes, what? _____ ◯ No

20. Favorite thing hanging on your room wall? _____

1. Name? _____

2. ◯ Thick ◯ Thin ◯ Sicilian ◯ Stuffed?

3. What do U like in your H20? ◯ Lemon ◯ Lime ◯ Nothing

4. Ever been on television? ◯ Yes, why? _____ ◯ No

5. Who has it easier? ◯ Girls ◯ Boys

6. Chips: ◯ Sour cream/onion ◯ Barbeque ◯ Cheddar ◯ Plain?

7. Favorite flavor of jelly, jam or preserves?_____

8. In a long line, do U ◯ look at your watch ◯ mumble aloud ◯ wait patiently?

9. ◯ Banana ◯ Banana nut bread ◯ Banana cream pie?

10. Is it hard for you to say U R sorry? ◯ Yes ◯ No

11. ◯ Scrambled ◯ Fried ◯ Poached ◯ Hard-boiled ◯ None?

12. Most boring book you've ever read?_____

13. Favorite kind of meat?_____

14. Fav movie food? ◯ Popcorn ◯ Twizzlers ◯ Nachos ◯ Other _____?

15. What TV show would you like to star in?_____

16. What's something you love that most people hate? _____

17. Ever think U R crazy? ◯ All the time ◯ Sometimes ◯ No, everyone else is!

18. Favorite junk food?_____

19. Do you take naps? ◯ Yes ◯ No

20. ◯ Original ◯ Extra crispy ◯ Spicy?

Word I don't like?

blood.

1. First name spelled backwards? . . . .

2. Last movie U saw? . . . .

3. ◯ Taco ◯ Burrito ◯ Enchilada ◯ Fajita?

4. What's your ring tone on your cell phone? . . . .

5. What's the most popular color in your wardrobe? . . . .

6. Coolest Arctic animal? ◯ Penguin ◯ Polar bear ◯ Harp seal ◯ Killer whale

7. R U usually ◯ too hot ◯ too cold?

8. R U allergic to anything? ◯ Yes, what? . . . . ◯ No

9. Favorite CD at the moment? . . . .

10. Is it hard for U to say U R wrong? ◯ Yes ◯ No

11. Favorite TV actor? . . . .

12. Favorite TV actress? . . . .

13. Least favorite class in school? . . . .

14. Ever entered through a "Do Not Enter" door? ◯ Yes ◯ No

15. What's a word you don't like? . . . .

16. How did U meet your BF? . . . .

17. What celebrity would U not trade places with? . . . .

18. Do you study ◯ in a quiet room ◯ with music on ◯ with TV on?

19. How many pairs of shoes do U own? ◯ 10 or fewer ◯ 10-20 ◯ 20 plus

20. Favorite sandwich? . . . .

1. My name is _____

2. I wish my name were _____

3. Ever been embarrassed by parents? ◯ Yes ◯ No

4. Any details 4 #3? _____

5. What famous person would you trade places with? _____

6. If you could invent something, what would it be? _____

7. How many teeth do you have? _____

8. Whiten your teeth? ◯ Yes, over-the-counter ◯ Yes, professionally ◯ No

9. How many times a day do you brush your teeth? _____

10. Rules should be ◯ followed ◯ used as guidelines ◯ broken

11. Worst fashion mistake you've ever made? _____

12. Most annoying thing about school? _____

13. Best thing about school? _____

14. Do you exercise? ◯ Yes ◯ No ◯ Sometimes

15. If yes to #14, what kind? _____

16. Most outrageous thing you've ever eaten? _____

17. ◯ Pay now, play later ◯ Play now, pay later?

18. Little kids are ◯ fun ◯ annoying?

19. Write papers ◯ in advance ◯ a few days before ◯ night before?

20. Study ◯ alone ◯ with a friend ◯ in a group?

1. First, middle, & last name . . . .

2. Read instructions before putting something together? ◯ Yes ◯ No

3. Favorite grade in school is/was . . . .

4. Coolest adult you know? . . . .

5. ◯ Small town ◯ Big city? Gotta fav? . . . .

6. Easiest person to buy a gift for? . . . .

7. ◯ Real Mayo ◯ Light Mayo ◯ Fat Free ◯ Yuck!

8. Favorite spuds R ◯ french fries ◯ home fries ◯ baked ◯ chips?

9. Which is worse? ◯ Brussel sprouts ◯ Spinach

10. Do you like foreign films? ◯ Yes ◯ No, subtitles drive me crazy!

11. Ever been caught with your fly down? ◯ Yes ◯ No

12. Ever had bathroom tissue stuck to your shoe? ◯ Yes ◯ No

13. Ever forget to remove a price tag from your clothing? ◯ Yes ◯ No

14. What do you think of when you hear the word **orange?** . . . .

15. Who do you think of when you see the color **red?** . . . .

16. Most peaceful color? . . . .

17. Walk under ladders? ◯ Yes ◯ No

18. Open umbrellas indoors? ◯ Yes ◯ No

19. Have you ever fallen down in public? ◯ Yes ◯ No

20. Smartest person you know . . . .

1. Your name please _____

2. Last time you read a newspaper? _____

3. Last time you opened a dictionary? _____

4. Last thing you cooked? _____

5. Favorite room in the house/apartment? _____

6. Favorite decorating style? _____

7. Describe your style of dressing _____

8. R U having a ◯ good hair day ◯ bad hair day ◯ so-so hair day?

9. Do you wear your friends' clothes? ◯ Yes ◯ No

10. Who encourages you the most? _____

11. Can you name all of Santa's reindeer? ◯ Yes ◯ No

12. Did you say yes? Go ahead then. _____

13. Do you like egg nog? ◯ Yes ◯ No

14. Favorite holiday treat? _____

15. R U squeamish? ◯ Yes ◯ No

16. If yes, what makes you squeamish? _____

17. R U an adventurous eater? _____

18. Camping: ◯ tent ◯ cabin ◯ RV

19. Ever encounter a wild animal? ◯ Yes, what? _____ ◯ No

20. Favorite amusement park? _____

Best personality trait?
Loyalty

1. My initials are _____

2. Favorite kind of dog? _____

3. Your worst personality trait? _____

4. Your best personality trait? _____

5. I know a lot about _____

6. I know absolutely nothing about _____

7. Holidays are ◯ fun with my family ◯ a nightmare with my family

8. Most embarrassing moment ever was _____

9. What have U dreamed of doing, but think U can't? _____

10. Why? _____

11. Any new goals? ◯ Yes, what? _____ ◯ No

12. Ever reached a goal? ◯ Yes, what? _____ ◯ No

13. ◯ I love waking up to birds ◯ I hate birds waking me up

14. Bedtime rituals? ◯ Yes, what?_____ ◯ No

15. Morning rituals? ◯ Yes, what?_____ ◯ No

16. R U a sucker for a happy ending? ◯ Yes ◯ No

17. Who taught you how to tie your shoes? _____

18. Do you know who your Dad's hero is? ◯ Yes, who_____ ◯ No

19. How about your Mom's? ◯ Yes, who_____ ◯ No

20. Who's your hero? _____

What kind of fries do I like?
It doesn't matter as long as I have ketchup.

1. My name is . . . .

2. Do you believe in magic? ◯ Yes ◯ No

3. Worst thing U have ever eaten? . . . .

4. Movie U can watch over and over? . . . .

5. Worst show on T.V. right now? . . . .

6. Ever pretend to love a gift that you really hated? ◯ Yes ◯ No

7. French fries: ◯ thin ◯ crinkle cut ◯ steak ◯ waffle?

8. Bagel: ◯ plain ◯ whole wheat ◯ sweet ◯ everything?

9. More about your bagel: ◯ naked ◯ cream cheese?

10. ◯ Board games ◯ Bored with games?

11. If safety weren't a problem, what animal would U have as a pet? . . . .

12. Favorite number? . . . .

13. Best advice anyone ever gave you? . . . .

14. Worst advice anyone ever gave you? . . . .

15. Ever stay up all night watching movies? ◯ Yes ◯ No

16. Ever stay up all night talking to a friend on the phone? ◯ Yes ◯ No

17. Do you order stuff on the Internet? ◯ Yes ◯ No

18. What "super sense" would U like? ◯ Hearing ◯ Sight ◯ Smell

19. What fashion item defines you? . . . .

20. Like what you are wearing right now? ◯ Yes ◯ No

1. My friends call me _____
   (name)

2. I get my music from ◯ the store ◯ online ◯ both

3. Describe your BF in 1 word _____

4. Ever want to be a d.j. on the radio? ◯ Yes ◯ No

5. If yes, what music would you play? _____

6. Do U wear green on St. Patrick's Day? ◯ Yes ◯ No

7. Do U miss kid stuff like hunting Easter eggs? ◯ Yes ◯ No

8. How about putting your tooth under your pillow? ◯ Yes ◯ No

9. Do you know what T.T.F.N. stands 4? ◯ Yes, what?_____ ◯ No

10. How do U get a song out of your head? _____

11. What do U splurge on? _____

12. Which describes you best? ◯ Emotional ◯ Logical ◯ 50/50

13. R U ◯ extroverted ◯ introverted ◯ somewhere in the middle?

14. I prefer a ◯ picnic in the park ◯ great night out

15. Most boring sport to watch? _____

16. What celebrity your BFF would identify U with? _____

17. Ever had a premonition? ◯ Yes ◯ No

18. How would your parents describe you? _____

19. U find $50. You ◯ bank it ◯ spend it ◯ try to find its owner

20. What did you watch on TV last night? _____

Robot?
I think I'll have one to do the things I hate!

1. The name I was born with is . . . .

2. How would U spend $1000 in 1 day? . . . .

3. What have you planned that became a disaster? . . . .

4. Do U have a profle on MYSPACE? ◯ Yes ◯ No

5. Favorite book character? . . . .

6. Best band since you were born? . . . .

7. I lose track of time when I . . . .

8. Do you think you will own a robot in the future? ◯ Yes ◯ No

9. Your friends come to U when they need a ◯ pep talk ◯ reality check

10. What do U do in your spare time? . . . .

11. Do you talk 2 your pet like it's a person? ◯ Yes ◯ No

12. ◯ Spend more time dwelling on the past ◯ Looking toward the future?

13. How long do you think civilization will last? . . . .

14. Lesson you've learned the hard way? . . . .

15. Where R U right now? . . . .

16. Who are U sitting next 2 right now? . . . .

17. How many times do you hit Snooze? . . . .

18. What do U think happens to your soul when you die? . . . .

19. Can U Yo-Yo? ◯ Yes ◯ No ◯ Who cares

20. Do U like being in the spotlight? ◯ Always ◯ Sometimes ◯ Never

1. Name on your birth certificate? _____

2. Day of the week, date, and time of your birth? _____

3. First word you said? _____

4. Most beautiful sounding language? _____

5. Feel like you're in control of your life? ◯ Yes ◯ No

6. Do U read the label on food before U buy? ◯ Yes ◯ No

7. Who do you trust with the deep stuff? _____

8. When U R mad, do U ◯ yell ◯ cry ◯ get quiet?

9. Best memory U have? _____

10. Worst memory U have? _____

11. ◯ Make quick decisions ◯ Think about it ◯ Avoid making decisions?

12. Any regrets? ◯ Yes, what?_____ ◯ No

13. If U had an extra hour every day, what would U do? _____

14. Describe a typical Saturday a.m. _____

15. Ever flown in a helicopter? ◯ Yes ◯ No

16. Something most people don't know about U? _____

17. ◯ Green thumb ◯ Kill everything ◯ Never tried to grow anything?

18. ◯ Daisies ◯ Roses ◯ Other _____?

19. Which is worse? ◯ Paper cut ◯ Burning your tongue?

20. I'm like ◯ my mom ◯ my dad ◯ neither — I might be an alien!

1. List all the names you go by _____

2. One word to describe you? _____

3. ◯ Unicorn   ◯ Pegasus   ◯ Dragon   ◯ Other _____

4. Ever rode on the handlebars of a bike?   ◯ Yes   ◯ No

5. What's outside your window right now? _____

6. What kind of student R U?   ◯ Great   ◯ So-so   ◯ Not-so-good

7. Who makes you laugh the hardest? _____

8. Who is your favorite superhero? _____

9. What would U like to be remembered 4? _____

10. Ever had surgery?   ◯ Yes, what kind? _____   ◯ No

11. Favorite movie song? _____

12. What's something that amazes U? _____

13. What do U sweeten with? ◯Pink stuff ◯Blue stuff ◯ Yellow stuff◯ Real stuff

14. Read anything good lately?   ◯ Yes, what? _____   ◯ No

15. Can you whistle a tune?   ◯ Of course   ◯ A little bit   ◯ No

16. One word to describe girls? _____

17. One word to describe boys? _____

18. Mountains: ◯ s'mores next to the fire   ◯ climbing rocks   ◯ hiking on trails?

19. Something legal U R addicted to? _____

20. Weirdest movie you've ever seen? _____

What word do I always misspell?

Necessary

1. Last name?. . . . .

2. What do U want to B when U grow up? . . . .

3. Ever enter a competition? ⃝ Yes, what? . . . . ⃝ No

4. Did you win? ⃝ Yes, what? . . . . ⃝ Nah

5. What's your typical Sunday morning? . . . .

6. What's something U R proud of? . . . .

7. What word do U always mispell? . . . .

8. Scared of heights? ⃝ Yes ⃝ No

9. Favorite chewing gum or mint? . . . .

10. Can you use chopsticks? ⃝ Yes ⃝ No

11. What perfume/cologne do you wear? . . . .

12. ⃝ Chocolate cake with chocolate icing ⃝ Angel food cake with fruit?

13. ⃝ Pencil ⃝ Mechanical pencil ⃝ Ballpoint ⃝ Gel pen?

14. Which is worse? ⃝ Headache ⃝ Toothache ⃝ Stomachache ⃝ Backache

15. ⃝ 4.0 GPA for a year ⃝ Spending time with your crush for a year

16. What piece(s) of jewelry do U always wear? . . . .

17. What do you love about summer? . . . .

18. ⃝ Green tea ⃝ Hot tea ⃝ Iced tea ⃝ Tea cookies?

19. Ever baked a cake? ⃝ Yes ⃝ No

20. Do you believe in ⃝ fate ⃝ God ⃝ yourself?

FAVORITE
FROZEN
TREAT?

ORANGE
POPSICLE

1. First name? ◯ Yes, what is it? . . . . ◯ No

2. If U could only go to 1 concert this year, who would U see? . . . .

3. Describe the watch you're wearing. . . . .

4. Rank in order of liking: __ Eagle __ Horse __ Cheetah __ Dolphin __ Pig

5. 😄 R U good at telling jokes? ◯ Yes ◯ No

6. Think life is ◯ fair ◯ unfair ◯ what you make it?

7. Which would U play? ◯ Damsel in distress ◯ Superhero ◯ Super villain?

8. What's your biggest question about life? . . . .

9. Ever in a school play? ◯ Yes, who/what were you? . . . . ◯ No

10. Do U listen to ◯ the words in music ◯ just the music?

11. Have a fav cartoon? ◯ Yes, what? . . . . ◯ No, don't watch anymore

12. What's cutest? ◯ Puppies ◯ Kittens ◯ Other . . . .

13. Favorite character from an animated movie? . . . .

14. Weirdest animal you've ever seen? . . . .

15. ◯ Aqua ◯ Fuchsia ◯ Mint ◯ Black ◯ Cream ◯ Violet

16. Favorite clothing brand? . . . .

17. Favorite cold beverage? . . . .

18. Your friends would describe U as ◯ sweet ◯ reliable ◯ crazy

19. Favorite frozen treat? . . . .

20. What would you like to be doing 10 years from now? . . . .

Pet trick?
My cat fetches.

1. Name _____ I wish it were _____

2. Do U feel sorry 4 the bad singers on American Idol? ◯ Yes ◯ No

3. When U talk on the phone do U: ◯ pace ◯ use hand gestures ◯ both?

4. Do you laugh when you hit your funny bone? ◯ Yes ◯ No

5. Vacation time! ◯ Big city ◯ Warm beach ◯ Another country

6. Do you like to read poetry? ◯ Yes ◯ Not really

7. R U known 4 your ◯ sense of humor ◯ good taste ◯ talent?

8. What duo R U & your bff most like? ◯ Batman & Robin ◯ Scooby & Shaggy

9. You love ◯ a little make-up ◯ a lot of make-up

10. R U ◯ Miss Adventure ◯ Miss Understood ◯ Miss Informed?

11. Favorite vegetable? _____

12. ◯ Fast food ◯ Themed restaurant ◯ Fine dining?

13. What do U do when you can't sleep? _____

14. Your dream machine is ◯ biggest SUV ◯ smallest sports car ◯ limo

15. ◯ Mac ◯ PC

16. Ever been a member of a fan club? ◯ Yes, which one? _____ ◯ No

17. Do U have a celebrity autograph? ◯ Yes, who? _____ ◯ No

18. Do U tell people when they have food stuck in their teeth? ◯ Yes ◯ No

19. Have a pet that does a cool trick? ◯ Yes, what? _____ ◯ No

20. Favorite thing hanging on your room wall? _____

FAVORITE JUNK FOOD?
TWINKIES

1. Name? _____

2. ◯ Thick ◯ Thin ◯ Sicilian ◯ Stuffed?

3. What do U like in your H20? ◯ Lemon ◯ Lime ◯ Nothing

4. Ever been on television? ◯ Yes, why? _____ ◯ No

5. Who has it easier? ◯ Girls ◯ Boys

6. Chips: ◯ Sour cream/onion ◯ Barbeque ◯ Cheddar ◯ Plain?

7. Favorite flavor of jelly, jam or preserves?_____

8. In a long line, do U ◯ look at your watch ◯ mumble aloud ◯ wait patiently?

9. ◯ Banana ◯ Banana nut bread ◯ Banana cream pie?

10. Is it hard for you to say U R sorry? ◯ Yes ◯ No

11. ◯ Scrambled ◯ Fried ◯ Poached ◯ Hard-boiled ◯ None?

12. Most boring book you've ever read?_____

13. Favorite kind of meat?_____

14. Fav movie food? ◯ Popcorn ◯ Twizzlers ◯ Nachos ◯ Other _____?

15. What TV show would you like to star in?_____

16. What's something you love that most people hate? _____

17. Ever think U R crazy? ◯ All the time ◯ Sometimes ◯ No, everyone else is!

18. Favorite junk food?_____

19. Do you take naps? ◯ Yes ◯ No

20. ◯ Original ◯ Extra crispy ◯ Spicy?

Word I don't like?

blood.

1. First name spelled backwards? . . . .

2. Last movie U saw? . . . .

3. ◯ Taco ◯ Burrito ◯ Enchilada ◯ Fajita?

4. What's your ring tone on your cell phone? . . . .

5. What's the most popular color in your wardrobe? . . . .

6. Coolest Arctic animal? ◯ Penguin ◯ Polar bear ◯ Harp seal ◯ Killer whale

7. R U usually ◯ too hot ◯ too cold?

8. R U allergic to anything? ◯ Yes, what? . . . . ◯ No

9. Favorite CD at the moment? . . . .

10. Is it hard for U to say U R wrong? ◯ Yes ◯ No

11. Favorite TV actor? . . . .

12. Favorite TV actress? . . . .

13. Least favorite class in school? . . . .

14. Ever entered through a "Do Not Enter" door? ◯ Yes ◯ No

15. What's a word you don't like? . . . .

16. How did U meet your BF? . . . .

17. What celebrity would U not trade places with? . . . .

18. Do you study ◯ in a quiet room ◯ with music on ◯ with TV on?

19. How many pairs of shoes do U own? ◯ 10 or fewer ◯ 10-20 ◯ 20 plus

20. Favorite sandwich? . . . .

If U could invent something, what would it B?
time machine

1. My name is _____

2. I wish my name were _____

3. Ever been embarrassed by parents? ◯ Yes ◯ No

4. Any details 4 #3? _____

5. What famous person would you trade places with? _____

6. If you could invent something, what would it be? _____

7. How many teeth do you have? _____

8. Whiten your teeth? ◯ Yes, over-the-counter ◯ Yes, professionally ◯ No

9. How many times a day do you brush your teeth? _____

10. Rules should be ◯ followed ◯ used as guidelines ◯ broken

11. Worst fashion mistake you've ever made? _____

12. Most annoying thing about school? _____

13. Best thing about school? _____

14. Do you exercise? ◯ Yes ◯ No ◯ Sometimes

15. If yes to #14, what kind? _____

16. Most outrageous thing you've ever eaten? _____

17. ◯ Pay now, play later ◯ Play now, pay later?

18. Little kids are ◯ fun ◯ annoying?

19. Write papers ◯ in advance ◯ a few days before ◯ night before?

20. Study ◯ alone ◯ with a friend ◯ in a group?

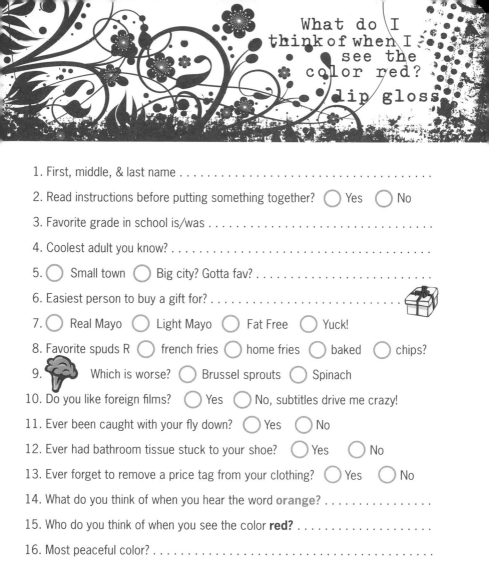

What do I think of when I see the color red? lip gloss

1. First, middle, & last name . . . .

2. Read instructions before putting something together? ◯ Yes ◯ No

3. Favorite grade in school is/was . . . .

4. Coolest adult you know? . . . .

5. ◯ Small town ◯ Big city? Gotta fav? . . . .

6. Easiest person to buy a gift for? . . . .

7. ◯ Real Mayo ◯ Light Mayo ◯ Fat Free ◯ Yuck!

8. Favorite spuds R ◯ french fries ◯ home fries ◯ baked ◯ chips?

9. Which is worse? ◯ Brussel sprouts ◯ Spinach

10. Do you like foreign films? ◯ Yes ◯ No, subtitles drive me crazy!

11. Ever been caught with your fly down? ◯ Yes ◯ No

12. Ever had bathroom tissue stuck to your shoe? ◯ Yes ◯ No

13. Ever forget to remove a price tag from your clothing? ◯ Yes ◯ No

14. What do you think of when you hear the word **orange?** . . . .

15. Who do you think of when you see the color **red?** . . . .

16. Most peaceful color? . . . .

17. Walk under ladders? ◯ Yes ◯ No

18. Open umbrellas indoors? ◯ Yes ◯ No

19. Have you ever fallen down in public? ◯ Yes ◯ No

20. Smartest person you know . . . .

1. Your name please _____

2. Last time you read a newspaper? _____

3. Last time you opened a dictionary? _____

4. Last thing you cooked? _____

5. Favorite room in the house/apartment? _____

6. Favorite decorating style? _____

7. Describe your style of dressing _____

8. R U having a ◯ good hair day ◯ bad hair day ◯ so-so hair day?

9. Do you wear your friends' clothes? ◯ Yes ◯ No

10. Who encourages you the most? _____

11. Can you name all of Santa's reindeer? ◯ Yes ◯ No

12. Did you say yes? Go ahead then. _____

13. Do you like egg nog? ◯ Yes ◯ No

14. Favorite holiday treat? _____

15. R U squeamish? ◯ Yes ◯ No

16. If yes, what makes you squeamish? _____

17. R U an adventurous eater? _____

18. Camping: ◯ tent ◯ cabin ◯ RV

19. Ever encounter a wild animal? ◯ Yes, what? _____ ◯ No

20. Favorite amusement park? _____

1. My initials are _____

2. Favorite kind of dog? _____

3. Your worst personality trait? _____

4. Your best personality trait? _____

5. I know a lot about _____

6. I know absolutely nothing about _____

7. Holidays are ◯ fun with my family ◯ a nightmare with my family

8. Most embarrassing moment ever was _____

9. What have U dreamed of doing, but think U can't? _____

10. Why? _____

11. Any new goals? ◯ Yes, what? _____ ◯ No

12. Ever reached a goal? ◯ Yes, what? _____ ◯ No

13. ◯ I love waking up to birds ◯ I hate birds waking me up

14. Bedtime rituals? ◯ Yes, what?_____ ◯ No

15. Morning rituals? ◯ Yes, what?_____ ◯ No

16. R U a sucker for a happy ending? ◯ Yes ◯ No

17. Who taught you how to tie your shoes? _____

18. Do you know who your Dad's hero is? ◯ Yes, who_____ ◯ No

19. How about your Mom's? ◯ Yes, who_____ ◯ No

20. Who's your hero? _____

What kind of fries do I like? It doesn't matter as long as I have ketchup.

★ ★ ★ ★ ★

1. My name is . . . .

2. Do you believe in magic? ◯ Yes   ◯ No

3. Worst thing U have ever eaten? . . . .

4. Movie U can watch over and over? . . . .

5. Worst show on T.V. right now? . . . .

6. Ever pretend to love a gift that you really hated? ◯ Yes ◯ No

7. French fries: ◯ thin ◯ crinkle cut ◯ steak ◯ waffle?

8. Bagel: ◯ plain ◯ whole wheat ◯ sweet ◯ everything?

9. More about your bagel: ◯ naked ◯ cream cheese?

10. ◯ Board games ◯ Bored with games?

11. If safety weren't a problem, what animal would U have as a pet? . . . .

12. Favorite number? . . . .

13. Best advice anyone ever gave you? . . . .

14. Worst advice anyone ever gave you? . . . .

15. Ever stay up all night watching movies? ◯ Yes ◯ No

16. Ever stay up all night talking to a friend on the phone? ◯ Yes ◯ No

17. Do you order stuff on the Internet? ◯ Yes ◯ No

18. What "super sense" would U like? ◯ Hearing ◯ Sight ◯ Smell

19. What fashion item defines you? . . . .

20. Like what you are wearing right now? ◯ Yes ◯ No

1. My friends call me _____
   (name)

2. I get my music from ⚪ the store ⚪ online ⚪ both

3. Describe your BF in 1 word _____

4. Ever want to be a d.j. on the radio? ⚪ Yes ⚪ No

5. If yes, what music would you play? _____

6. 🍀 Do U wear green on St. Patrick's Day? ⚪ Yes ⚪ No

7. Do U miss kid stuff like hunting Easter eggs? ⚪ Yes ⚪ No

8. How about putting your tooth under your pillow? ⚪ Yes ⚪ No

9. Do you know what T.T.F.N. stands 4? ⚪ Yes, what?_____ ⚪ No

10. How do U get a song out of your head? _____

11. What do U splurge on? _____

12. Which describes you best? ⚪ Emotional ⚪ Logical ⚪ 50/50

13. R U ⚪ extroverted ⚪ introverted ⚪ somewhere in the middle?

14. I prefer a ⚪ picnic in the park ⚪ great night out

15. Most boring sport to watch? _____

16. What celebrity your BFF would identify U with? _____

17. Ever had a premonition? ⚪ Yes ⚪ No

18. How would your parents describe you? _____

19. U find $50. You ⚪ bank it ⚪ spend it ⚪ try to find its owner

20. What did you watch on TV last night? _____

Robot?
I think I'll have one to do the things I hate!

1. The name I was born with is . . . .
2. How would U spend $1000 in 1 day? . . . .
3. What have you planned that became a disaster? . . . .
4. Do U have a profile on MYSPACE? ◯ Yes ◯ No
5. Favorite book character? . . . .
6. Best band since you were born? . . . .
7. I lose track of time when I . . . .
8. Do you think you will own a robot in the future? ◯ Yes ◯ No
9. Your friends come to U when they need a ◯ pep talk ◯ reality check
10. What do U do in your spare time? . . . .
11. Do you talk 2 your pet like it's a person? ◯ Yes ◯ No
12. ◯ Spend more time dwelling on the past ◯ Looking toward the future?
13. How long do you think civilization will last? . . . .
14. Lesson you've learned the hard way? . . . .
15. Where R U right now? . . . .
16. Who are U sitting next 2 right now? . . . .
17. How many times do you hit Snooze? . . . .
18. What do U think happens to your soul when you die? . . . .
19. Can U Yo-Yo? ◯ Yes ◯ No ◯ Who cares
20. Do U like being in the spotlight? ◯ Always ◯ Sometimes ◯ Never

1. Name on your birth certificate? _____

2. Day of the week, date, and time of your birth? _____

3. First word you said? _____

4. Most beautiful sounding language? _____

5. Feel like you're in control of your life? ○ Yes ○ No

6. Do U read the label on food before U buy? ○ Yes ○ No

7. Who do you trust with the deep stuff? _____

8. When U R mad, do U ○ yell ○ cry ○ get quiet?

9. Best memory U have? _____

10. Worst memory U have? _____

11. ○ Make quick decisions ○ Think about it ○ Avoid making decisions?

12. Any regrets? ○ Yes, what?_____ ○ No

13. If U had an extra hour every day, what would U do? _____

14. Describe a typical Saturday a.m. _____

15. Ever flown in a helicopter? ○ Yes ○ No

16. Something most people don't know about U? _____

17. ○ Green thumb ○ Kill everything ○ Never tried to grow anything?

18. ○ Daisies ○ Roses ○ Other _____ ?

19. Which is worse? ○ Paper cut ○ Burning your tongue?

20. I'm like ○ my mom ○ my dad ○ neither — I might be an alien!

Something legal I'm addicted to? Diet Coke.

1. List all the names you go by _____

2. One word to describe you? _____

3. ⚪ Unicorn ⚪ Pegasus ⚪ Dragon ⚪ Other _____

4. Ever rode on the handlebars of a bike? ⚪ Yes ⚪ No

5. What's outside your window right now? _____

6. What kind of student R U? ⚪ Great ⚪ So-so ⚪ Not-so-good

7. Who makes you laugh the hardest? _____

8. Who is your favorite superhero? _____

9. What would U like to be remembered 4? _____

10. Ever had surgery? ⚪ Yes, what kind? _____ ⚪ No

11. Favorite movie song? _____

12. What's something that amazes U? _____

13. What do U sweeten with? ⚪Pink stuff ⚪Blue stuff ⚪ Yellow stuff⚪ Real stuff

14. Read anything good lately? ⚪ Yes, what? _____ ⚪ No

15. Can you whistle a tune? ⚪ Of course ⚪ A little bit ⚪ No

16. One word to describe girls? _____

17. One word to describe boys? _____

18. Mountains: ⚪ s'mores next to the fire ⚪ climbing rocks ⚪ hiking on trails?

19. Something legal U R addicted to? _____

20. Weirdest movie you've ever seen? _____

What word do I always misspell?

Necessary

1. Last name?. . . . .

2. What do U want to B when U grow up? . . . .

3. Ever enter a competition? ◯ Yes, what? . . . . ◯ No

4. Did you win? ◯ Yes, what? . . . . ◯ Nah

5. What's your typical Sunday morning? . . . .

6. What's something U R proud of? . . . .

7. What word do U always mispell? . . . .

8. Scared of heights? ◯ Yes ◯ No

9. Favorite chewing gum or mint? . . . .

10. Can you use chopsticks? ◯ Yes ◯ No

11. What perfume/cologne do you wear? . . . .

12. ◯ Chocolate cake with chocolate icing ◯ Angel food cake with fruit?

13. ◯ Pencil ◯ Mechanical pencil ◯ Ballpoint ◯ Gel pen?

14. Which is worse? ◯ Headache ◯ Toothache ◯ Stomachache ◯ Backache

15. ◯ 4.0 GPA for a year ◯ Spending time with your crush for a year

16. What piece(s) of jewelry do U always wear? . . . .

17. What do you love about summer? . . . .

18. ◯ Green tea ◯ Hot tea ◯ Iced tea ◯ Tea cookies?

19. Ever baked a cake? ◯ Yes ◯ No

20. Do you believe in ◯ fate ◯ God ◯ yourself?

FAVORITE
FROZEN
TREAT?
ORANGE
POPSICLE

1. First name? ◯ Yes, what is it? . . . . ◯ No

2. If U could only go to 1 concert this year, who would U see? . . . .

3. Describe the watch you're wearing. . . . .

4. Rank in order of liking: __ Eagle __ Horse __ Cheetah __ Dolphin __ Pig

5. 😄 R U good at telling jokes? ◯ Yes ◯ No

6. Think life is ◯ fair ◯ unfair ◯ what you make it?

7. Which would U play? ◯ Damsel in distress ◯ Superhero ◯ Super villain?

8. What's your biggest question about life? . . . .

9. Ever in a school play? ◯ Yes, who/what were you? . . . . ◯ No

10. Do U listen to ◯ the words in music ◯ just the music?

11. Have a fav cartoon? ◯ Yes, what? . . . . ◯ No, don't watch anymore

12. What's cutest? ◯ Puppies ◯ Kittens ◯ Other . . . .

13. Favorite character from an animated movie? . . . .

14. Weirdest animal you've ever seen? . . . .

15. ◯ Aqua ◯ Fuchsia ◯ Mint ◯ Black ◯ Cream ◯ Violet

16. Favorite clothing brand? . . . .

17. Favorite cold beverage? . . . .

18. Your friends would describe U as ◯ sweet ◯ reliable ◯ crazy

19. Favorite frozen treat? . . . .

20. What would you like to be doing 10 years from now? . . . .

Pet trick?
My cat fetches.

1. Name _____ I wish it were _____

2. Do U feel sorry 4 the bad singers on American Idol? ◯ Yes ◯ No

3. When U talk on the phone do U: ◯ pace ◯ use hand gestures ◯ both?

4. Do you laugh when you hit your funny bone? ◯ Yes ◯ No

5. Vacation time! ◯ Big city ◯ Warm beach ◯ Another country

6. Do you like to read poetry? ◯ Yes ◯ Not really

7. R U known 4 your ◯ sense of humor ◯ good taste ◯ talent?

8. What duo R U & your bff most like? ◯ Batman & Robin ◯ Scooby & Shaggy

9. You love ◯ a little make-up ◯ a lot of make-up

10. R U ◯ Miss Adventure ◯ Miss Understood ◯ Miss Informed?

11. Favorite vegetable? _____

12. ◯ Fast food ◯ Themed restaurant ◯ Fine dining?

13. What do U do when you can't sleep? _____

14. Your dream machine is ◯ biggest SUV ◯ smallest sports car ◯ limo

15. ◯ Mac ◯ PC

16. Ever been a member of a fan club? ◯ Yes, which one? _____ ◯ No

17. Do U have a celebrity autograph? ◯ Yes, who? _____ ◯ No

18. Do U tell people when they have food stuck in their teeth? ◯ Yes ◯ No

19. Have a pet that does a cool trick? ◯ Yes, what? _____ ◯ No

20. Favorite thing hanging on your room wall? _____

1. Name? _____

2. ◯ Thick ◯ Thin ◯ Sicilian ◯ Stuffed?

3. What do U like in your H20? ◯ Lemon ◯ Lime ◯ Nothing

4. Ever been on television? ◯ Yes, why? _____ ◯ No

5. Who has it easier? ◯ Girls ◯ Boys

6. Chips: ◯ Sour cream/onion ◯ Barbeque ◯ Cheddar ◯ Plain?

7. Favorite flavor of jelly, jam or preserves?_____

8. In a long line, do U ◯ look at your watch ◯ mumble aloud ◯ wait patiently?

9. ◯ Banana ◯ Banana nut bread ◯ Banana cream pie?

10. Is it hard for you to say U R sorry? ◯ Yes ◯ No

11. ◯ Scrambled ◯ Fried ◯ Poached ◯ Hard-boiled ◯ None?

12. Most boring book you've ever read?_____

13. Favorite kind of meat?_____

14. Fav movie food? ◯ Popcorn ◯ Twizzlers ◯ Nachos ◯ Other _____?

15. What TV show would you like to star in?_____

16. What's something you love that most people hate? _____

17. Ever think U R crazy? ◯ All the time ◯ Sometimes ◯ No, everyone else is!

18. Favorite junk food?_____

19. Do you take naps? ◯ Yes ◯ No

20. ◯ Original ◯ Extra crispy ◯ Spicy?

Word I don't like?

blood.

1. First name spelled backwards? . . . .

2. Last movie U saw? . . . .

3. ◯ Taco   ◯ Burrito   ◯ Enchilada   ◯ Fajita?

4. What's your ring tone on your cell phone? . . . .

5. What's the most popular color in your wardrobe? . . . .

6. Coolest Arctic animal? ◯ Penguin ◯ Polar bear ◯ Harp seal ◯ Killer whale

7. R U usually ◯ too hot   ◯ too cold?

8. R U allergic to anything? ◯ Yes, what? . . . . ◯ No

9. Favorite CD at the moment? . . . .

10. Is it hard for U to say U R wrong? ◯ Yes   ◯ No

11. Favorite TV actor? . . . .

12. Favorite TV actress? . . . .

13. Least favorite class in school? . . . .

14. Ever entered through a "Do Not Enter" door? ◯ Yes ◯ No

15. What's a word you don't like? . . . .

16. How did U meet your BF? . . . .

17. What celebrity would U not trade places with? . . . .

18. Do you study ◯ in a quiet room   ◯ with music on   ◯ with TV on?

19. How many pairs of shoes do U own? ◯ 10 or fewer ◯ 10-20 ◯ 20 plus

20. Favorite sandwich? . . . .

If U could invent something, what would it B?
time machine

1. My name is _____

2. I wish my name were _____

3. Ever been embarrassed by parents? ◯ Yes ◯ No

4. Any details 4 #3? _____

5. What famous person would you trade places with? _____

6. If you could invent something, what would it be? _____

7. How many teeth do you have? _____

8. Whiten your teeth? ◯ Yes, over-the-counter ◯ Yes, professionally ◯ No

9. How many times a day do you brush your teeth? _____

10. Rules should be ◯ followed ◯ used as guidelines ◯ broken

11. Worst fashion mistake you've ever made? _____

12. Most annoying thing about school? _____

13. Best thing about school? _____

14. Do you exercise? ◯ Yes ◯ No ◯ Sometimes

15. If yes to #14, what kind? _____

16. Most outrageous thing you've ever eaten? _____

17. ◯ Pay now, play later ◯ Play now, pay later?

18. Little kids are ◯ fun ◯ annoying?

19. Write papers ◯ in advance ◯ a few days before ◯ night before?

20. Study ◯ alone ◯ with a friend ◯ in a group?

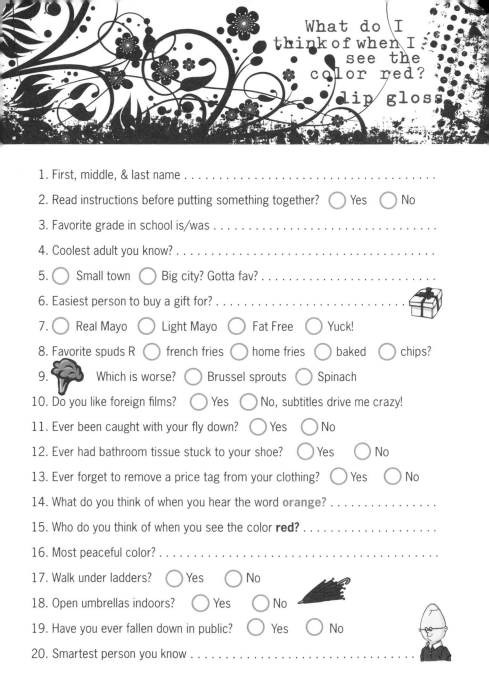

What do I think of when I see the color red? lip gloss

1. First, middle, & last name . . . .

2. Read instructions before putting something together? ◯ Yes ◯ No

3. Favorite grade in school is/was . . . .

4. Coolest adult you know? . . . .

5. ◯ Small town ◯ Big city? Gotta fav? . . . .

6. Easiest person to buy a gift for? . . . .

7. ◯ Real Mayo ◯ Light Mayo ◯ Fat Free ◯ Yuck!

8. Favorite spuds R ◯ french fries ◯ home fries ◯ baked ◯ chips?

9. Which is worse? ◯ Brussel sprouts ◯ Spinach

10. Do you like foreign films? ◯ Yes ◯ No, subtitles drive me crazy!

11. Ever been caught with your fly down? ◯ Yes ◯ No

12. Ever had bathroom tissue stuck to your shoe? ◯ Yes ◯ No

13. Ever forget to remove a price tag from your clothing? ◯ Yes ◯ No

14. What do you think of when you hear the word **orange?** . . . .

15. Who do you think of when you see the color **red?** . . . .

16. Most peaceful color? . . . .

17. Walk under ladders? ◯ Yes ◯ No

18. Open umbrellas indoors? ◯ Yes ◯ No

19. Have you ever fallen down in public? ◯ Yes ◯ No

20. Smartest person you know . . . .

1. Your name please _____

2. Last time you read a newspaper? _____

3. Last time you opened a dictionary? _____

4. Last thing you cooked? _____

5. Favorite room in the house/apartment? _____

6. Favorite decorating style? _____

7. Describe your style of dressing _____

8. R U having a ◯ good hair day ◯ bad hair day ◯ so-so hair day?

9. Do you wear your friends' clothes? ◯ Yes ◯ No

10. Who encourages you the most? _____

11. Can you name all of Santa's reindeer? ◯ Yes ◯ No

12. Did you say yes? Go ahead then. _____

13. Do you like egg nog? ◯ Yes ◯ No

14. Favorite holiday treat? _____

15. R U squeamish? ◯ Yes ◯ No

16. If yes, what makes you squeamish? _____

17. R U an adventurous eater? _____

18. Camping: ◯ tent ◯ cabin ◯ RV

19. Ever encounter a wild animal? ◯ Yes, what? _____ ◯ No

20. Favorite amusement park? _____

Best personality trait?
Loyalty

1. My initials are _____

2. Favorite kind of dog? _____

3. Your worst personality trait? _____

4. Your best personality trait? _____

5. I know a lot about _____

6. I know absolutely nothing about _____

7. Holidays are ◯ fun with my family ◯ a nightmare with my family

8. Most embarrassing moment ever was _____

9. What have U dreamed of doing, but think U can't? _____

10. Why? _____

11. Any new goals? ◯ Yes, what? _____ ◯ No

12. Ever reached a goal? ◯ Yes, what? _____ ◯ No

13. ◯ I love waking up to birds ◯ I hate birds waking me up

14. Bedtime rituals? ◯ Yes, what?_____ ◯ No

15. Morning rituals? ◯ Yes, what?_____ ◯ No

16. R U a sucker for a happy ending? ◯ Yes ◯ No

17. Who taught you how to tie your shoes? _____

18. Do you know who your Dad's hero is? ◯ Yes, who_____ ◯ No

19. How about your Mom's? ◯ Yes, who_____ ◯ No

20. Who's your hero? _____

What kind of fries do I like?
It doesn't matter as long as I have ketchup.

★ ★ ★ ★ ★ ★

1. My name is . . . .

2. Do you believe in magic? ◯ Yes ◯ No

3. Worst thing U have ever eaten? . . . .

4. Movie U can watch over and over? . . . .

5. Worst show on T.V. right now? . . . .

6. Ever pretend to love a gift that you really hated? ◯ Yes ◯ No

7. French fries: ◯ thin ◯ crinkle cut ◯ steak ◯ waffle?

8. Bagel: ◯ plain ◯ whole wheat ◯ sweet ◯ everything?

9. More about your bagel: ◯ naked ◯ cream cheese?

10. ◯ Board games ◯ Bored with games?

11. If safety weren't a problem, what animal would U have as a pet? . . . .

12. Favorite number? . . . .

13. Best advice anyone ever gave you? . . . .

14. Worst advice anyone ever gave you? . . . .

15. Ever stay up all night watching movies? ◯ Yes ◯ No

16. Ever stay up all night talking to a friend on the phone? ◯ Yes ◯ No

17. Do you order stuff on the Internet? ◯ Yes ◯ No

18. What "super sense" would U like? ◯ Hearing ◯ Sight ◯ Smell

19. What fashion item defines you? . . . .

20. Like what you are wearing right now? ◯ Yes ◯ No

1. My friends call me _____
   (name)

2. I get my music from ◯ the store ◯ online ◯ both

3. Describe your BF in 1 word _____

4. Ever want to be a d.j. on the radio? ◯ Yes ◯ No

5. If yes, what music would you play? _____

6. 🍀 Do U wear green on St. Patrick's Day? ◯ Yes ◯ No

7. Do U miss kid stuff like hunting Easter eggs? ◯ Yes ◯ No

8. How about putting your tooth under your pillow? ◯ Yes ◯ No

9. Do you know what T.T.F.N. stands 4? ◯ Yes, what?_____ ◯ No

10. How do U get a song out of your head? _____

11. What do U splurge on? _____

12. Which describes you best? ◯ Emotional ◯ Logical ◯ 50/50

13. R U ◯ extroverted ◯ introverted ◯ somewhere in the middle?

14. I prefer a ◯ picnic in the park ◯ great night out

15. Most boring sport to watch? _____

16. What celebrity your BFF would identify U with? _____

17. Ever had a premonition? ◯ Yes ◯ No

18. How would your parents describe you? _____

19. U find $50. You ◯ bank it ◯ spend it ◯ try to find its owner

20. What did you watch on TV last night? _____

Robot?
I think I'll have one to do the things I hate!

1. The name I was born with is . . . .
2. How would U spend $1000 in 1 day? . . . .
3. What have you planned that became a disaster? . . . .
4. Do U have a profile on MYSPACE? ◯ Yes ◯ No
5. Favorite book character? . . . .
6. Best band since you were born? . . . .
7. I lose track of time when I . . . .
8. Do you think you will own a robot in the future? ◯ Yes ◯ No
9. Your friends come to U when they need a ◯ pep talk ◯ reality check
10. What do U do in your spare time? . . . .
11. Do you talk 2 your pet like it's a person? ◯ Yes ◯ No
12. ◯ Spend more time dwelling on the past ◯ Looking toward the future?
13. How long do you think civilization will last? . . . .
14. Lesson you've learned the hard way? . . . .
15. Where R U right now? . . . .
16. Who are U sitting next 2 right now? . . . .
17. How many times do you hit Snooze? . . . .
18. What do U think happens to your soul when you die? . . . .
19. ◯ Can U Yo-Yo? ◯ Yes ◯ No ◯ Who cares
20. Do U like being in the spotlight? ◯ Always ◯ Sometimes ◯ Never

1. Name on your birth certificate? _____

2. Day of the week, date, and time of your birth? _____

3. First word you said? _____

4. Most beautiful sounding language? _____

5. Feel like you're in control of your life? ◯ Yes ◯ No

6. Do U read the label on food before U buy? ◯ Yes ◯ No

7. Who do you trust with the deep stuff? _____

8. When U R mad, do U ◯ yell ◯ cry ◯ get quiet?

9. Best memory U have? _____

10. Worst memory U have? _____

11. ◯ Make quick decisions ◯ Think about it ◯ Avoid making decisions?

12. Any regrets? ◯ Yes, what?_____ ◯ No

13. If U had an extra hour every day, what would U do? _____

14. Describe a typical Saturday a.m. _____

15. Ever flown in a helicopter? ◯ Yes ◯ No

16. Something most people don't know about U? _____

17. ◯ Green thumb ◯ Kill everything ◯ Never tried to grow anything?

18. ◯ Daisies ◯ Roses ◯ Other _____ ?

19. Which is worse? ◯ Paper cut ◯ Burning your tongue?

20. I'm like ◯ my mom ◯ my dad ◯ neither — I might be an alien!

1. List all the names you go by _____

2. One word to describe you? _____

3. ◯ Unicorn   ◯ Pegasus   ◯ Dragon   ◯ Other _____

4. Ever rode on the handlebars of a bike?   ◯ Yes   ◯ No

5. What's outside your window right now? _____

6. What kind of student R U?   ◯ Great   ◯ So-so   ◯ Not-so-good

7. Who makes you laugh the hardest? _____

8. Who is your favorite superhero? _____

9. What would U like to be remembered 4? _____

10. Ever had surgery?   ◯ Yes, what kind? _____   ◯ No

11. Favorite movie song? _____

12. What's something that amazes U? _____

13. What do U sweeten with? ◯ Pink stuff ◯ Blue stuff ◯ Yellow stuff ◯ Real stuff

14. Read anything good lately?   ◯ Yes, what? _____   ◯ No

15. Can you whistle a tune?   ◯ Of course   ◯ A little bit   ◯ No

16. One word to describe girls? _____

17. One word to describe boys? _____

18. Mountains: ◯ s'mores next to the fire   ◯ climbing rocks   ◯ hiking on trails?

19. Something legal U R addicted to? _____

20. Weirdest movie you've ever seen? _____

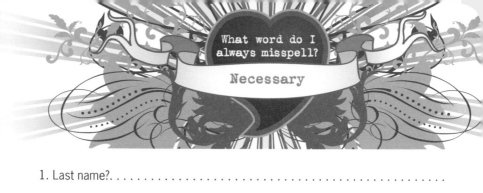

What word do I always misspell?

Necessary

1. Last name?. . . . .

2. What do U want to B when U grow up? . . . .

3. Ever enter a competition? ◯ Yes, what? . . . . ◯ No

4. Did you win? ◯ Yes, what? . . . . ◯ Nah

5. What's your typical Sunday morning? . . . .

6. What's something U R proud of? . . . .

7. What word do U always mispell? . . . .

8. Scared of heights? ◯ Yes ◯ No

9. Favorite chewing gum or mint? . . . .

10. Can you use chopsticks? ◯ Yes ◯ No

11. What perfume/cologne do you wear? . . . .

12. ◯ Chocolate cake with chocolate icing ◯ Angel food cake with fruit?

13. ◯ Pencil ◯ Mechanical pencil ◯ Ballpoint ◯ Gel pen?

14. Which is worse? ◯ Headache ◯ Toothache ◯ Stomachache ◯ Backache

15. ◯ 4.0 GPA for a year ◯ Spending time with your crush for a year

16. What piece(s) of jewelry do U always wear? . . . .

17. What do you love about summer? . . . .

18. ◯ Green tea ◯ Hot tea ◯ Iced tea ◯ Tea cookies?

19. Ever baked a cake? ◯ Yes ◯ No

20. Do you believe in ◯ fate ◯ God ◯ yourself?

FAVORITE
FROZEN
TREAT?

ORANGE
POPSICLE

1. First name? ◯ Yes, what is it? . . . . ◯ No

2. If U could only go to 1 concert this year, who would U see? . . . .

3. Describe the watch you're wearing. . . . .

4. Rank in order of liking: __ Eagle __ Horse __ Cheetah __ Dolphin __ Pig

5. 😊 R U good at telling jokes? ◯ Yes ◯ No

6. Think life is ◯ fair ◯ unfair ◯ what you make it?

7. Which would U play? ◯ Damsel in distress ◯ Superhero ◯ Super villain?

8. What's your biggest question about life? . . . .

9. Ever in a school play? ◯ Yes, who/what were you? . . . . ◯ No

10. Do U listen to ◯ the words in music ◯ just the music?

11. Have a fav cartoon? ◯ Yes, what? . . . . ◯ No, don't watch anymore

12. What's cutest? ◯ Puppies ◯ Kittens ◯ Other . . . .

13. Favorite character from an animated movie? . . . .

14. Weirdest animal you've ever seen? . . . .

15. ◯ Aqua ◯ Fuchsia ◯ Mint ◯ Black ◯ Cream ◯ Violet

16. Favorite clothing brand? . . . .

17. Favorite cold beverage? . . . .

18. Your friends would describe U as ◯ sweet ◯ reliable ◯ crazy

19. Favorite frozen treat? . . . .

20. What would you like to be doing 10 years from now? . . . .

Pet trick?
My cat fetches.

1. Name _____ I wish it were _____

2. Do U feel sorry 4 the bad singers on American Idol? ◯ Yes ◯ No

3. When U talk on the phone do U: ◯ pace ◯ use hand gestures ◯ both?

4. Do you laugh when you hit your funny bone? ◯ Yes ◯ No

5. Vacation time! ◯ Big city ◯ Warm beach ◯ Another country

6. Do you like to read poetry? ◯ Yes ◯ Not really

7. R U known 4 your ◯ sense of humor ◯ good taste ◯ talent?

8. What duo R U & your bff most like? ◯ Batman & Robin ◯ Scooby & Shaggy

9. You love ◯ a little make-up ◯ a lot of make-up

10. R U ◯ Miss Adventure ◯ Miss Understood ◯ Miss Informed?

11. Favorite vegetable? _____

12. ◯ Fast food ◯ Themed restaurant ◯ Fine dining?

13. What do U do when you can't sleep? _____

14. Your dream machine is ◯ biggest SUV ◯ smallest sports car ◯ limo

15. ◯ Mac ◯ PC

16. Ever been a member of a fan club? ◯ Yes, which one? _____ ◯ No

17. Do U have a celebrity autograph? ◯ Yes, who? _____ ◯ No

18. Do U tell people when they have food stuck in their teeth? ◯ Yes ◯ No

19. Have a pet that does a cool trick? ◯ Yes, what? _____ ◯ No

20. Favorite thing hanging on your room wall? _____

1. Name? _____

2. ◯ Thick   ◯ Thin   ◯ Sicilian   ◯ Stuffed?

3. What do U like in your H20?   ◯ Lemon   ◯ Lime   ◯ Nothing

4. Ever been on television?   ◯ Yes, why? _____   ◯ No

5. Who has it easier?   ◯ Girls   ◯ Boys

6. Chips: ◯ Sour cream/onion   ◯ Barbeque   ◯ Cheddar   ◯ Plain?

7. Favorite flavor of jelly, jam or preserves?_____

8. In a long line, do U   ◯ look at your watch   ◯ mumble aloud   ◯ wait patiently?

9. ◯ Banana   ◯ Banana nut bread   ◯ Banana cream pie?

10. Is it hard for you to say U R sorry?   ◯ Yes   ◯ No

11. ◯ Scrambled   ◯ Fried   ◯ Poached   ◯ Hard-boiled   ◯ None?

12. Most boring book you've ever read?_____

13. Favorite kind of meat?_____

14. Fav movie food?   ◯ Popcorn   ◯ Twizzlers   ◯ Nachos   ◯ Other _____?

15. What TV show would you like to star in?_____

16. What's something you love that most people hate? _____

17. Ever think U R crazy?   ◯ All the time   ◯ Sometimes   ◯ No, everyone else is!

18. Favorite junk food?_____

19. Do you take naps?   ◯ Yes   ◯ No

20. ◯ Original   ◯ Extra crispy   ◯ Spicy?

Word I don't like?

blood.

1. First name spelled backwards? . . . .

2. Last movie U saw? . . . .

3. ◯ Taco ◯ Burrito ◯ Enchilada ◯ Fajita?

4. What's your ring tone on your cell phone? . . . .

5. What's the most popular color in your wardrobe? . . . .

6. Coolest Arctic animal? ◯ Penguin ◯ Polar bear ◯ Harp seal ◯ Killer whale

7. R U usually ◯ too hot ◯ too cold?

8. R U allergic to anything? ◯ Yes, what? . . . . ◯ No

9. Favorite CD at the moment? . . . .

10. Is it hard for U to say U R wrong? ◯ Yes ◯ No

11. Favorite TV actor? . . . .

12. Favorite TV actress? . . . .

13. Least favorite class in school? . . . .

14. Ever entered through a "Do Not Enter" door? ◯ Yes ◯ No

15. What's a word you don't like? . . . .

16. How did U meet your BF? . . . .

17. What celebrity would U not trade places with? . . . .

18. Do you study ◯ in a quiet room ◯ with music on ◯ with TV on?

19. How many pairs of shoes do U own? ◯ 10 or fewer ◯ 10-20 ◯ 20 plus

20. Favorite sandwich? . . . .

1. My name is _____

2. I wish my name were _____

3. Ever been embarrassed by parents? ◯ Yes ◯ No

4. Any details 4 #3? _____

5. What famous person would you trade places with? _____

6. If you could invent something, what would it be? _____

7. How many teeth do you have? _____

8. Whiten your teeth? ◯ Yes, over-the-counter ◯ Yes, professionally ◯ No

9. How many times a day do you brush your teeth? _____

10. Rules should be ◯ followed ◯ used as guidelines ◯ broken

11. Worst fashion mistake you've ever made? _____

12. Most annoying thing about school? _____

13. Best thing about school? _____

14. Do you exercise? ◯ Yes ◯ No ◯ Sometimes

15. If yes to #14, what kind? _____

16. Most outrageous thing you've ever eaten? _____

17. ◯ Pay now, play later ◯ Play now, pay later?

18. Little kids are ◯ fun ◯ annoying?

19. Write papers ◯ in advance ◯ a few days before ◯ night before?

20. Study ◯ alone ◯ with a friend ◯ in a group?

1. First, middle, & last name . . . .

2. Read instructions before putting something together? ◯ Yes ◯ No

3. Favorite grade in school is/was . . . .

4. Coolest adult you know? . . . .

5. ◯ Small town ◯ Big city? Gotta fav? . . . .

6. Easiest person to buy a gift for? . . . .

7. ◯ Real Mayo ◯ Light Mayo ◯ Fat Free ◯ Yuck!

8. Favorite spuds R ◯ french fries ◯ home fries ◯ baked ◯ chips?

9. Which is worse? ◯ Brussel sprouts ◯ Spinach

10. Do you like foreign films? ◯ Yes ◯ No, subtitles drive me crazy!

11. Ever been caught with your fly down? ◯ Yes ◯ No

12. Ever had bathroom tissue stuck to your shoe? ◯ Yes ◯ No

13. Ever forget to remove a price tag from your clothing? ◯ Yes ◯ No

14. What do you think of when you hear the word **orange?** . . . .

15. Who do you think of when you see the color **red?** . . . .

16. Most peaceful color? . . . .

17. Walk under ladders? ◯ Yes ◯ No

18. Open umbrellas indoors? ◯ Yes ◯ No

19. Have you ever fallen down in public? ◯ Yes ◯ No

20. Smartest person you know . . . .

1. Your name please _____

2. Last time you read a newspaper? _____

3. Last time you opened a dictionary? _____

4. Last thing you cooked? _____

5. Favorite room in the house/apartment? _____

6. Favorite decorating style? _____

7. Describe your style of dressing _____

8. R U having a ◯ good hair day ◯ bad hair day ◯ so-so hair day?

9. Do you wear your friends' clothes? ◯ Yes ◯ No

10. Who encourages you the most? _____

11. Can you name all of Santa's reindeer? ◯ Yes ◯ No

12. Did you say yes? Go ahead then. _____

13. Do you like egg nog? ◯ Yes ◯ No

14. Favorite holiday treat? _____

15. R U squeamish? ◯ Yes ◯ No

16. If yes, what makes you squeamish? _____

17. R U an adventurous eater? _____

18. Camping: ◯ tent ◯ cabin ◯ RV

19. Ever encounter a wild animal? ◯ Yes, what? _____ ◯ No

20. Favorite amusement park? _____

Best personality trait?
Loyalty

1. My initials are _____

2. Favorite kind of dog? _____

3. Your worst personality trait? _____

4. Your best personality trait? _____

5. I know a lot about _____

6. I know absolutely nothing about _____

7. Holidays are ◯ fun with my family ◯ a nightmare with my family

8. Most embarrassing moment ever was _____

9. What have U dreamed of doing, but think U can't? _____

10. Why? _____

11. Any new goals? ◯ Yes, what? _____ ◯ No

12. Ever reached a goal? ◯ Yes, what? _____ ◯ No

13. ◯ I love waking up to birds ◯ I hate birds waking me up

14. Bedtime rituals? ◯ Yes, what?_____ ◯ No

15. Morning rituals? ◯ Yes, what?_____ ◯ No

16. R U a sucker for a happy ending? ◯ Yes ◯ No

17. Who taught you how to tie your shoes? _____

18. Do you know who your Dad's hero is? ◯ Yes, who_____ ◯ No

19. How about your Mom's? ◯ Yes, who_____ ◯ No

20. Who's your hero? _____

What kind of fries do I like?
It doesn't matter as long as I have ketchup.

★ ★ ★ ★ ★

1. My name is . . . .

2. Do you believe in magic? ◯ Yes ◯ No

3. Worst thing U have ever eaten? . . . .

4. Movie U can watch over and over? . . . .

5. Worst show on T.V. right now? . . . .

6. Ever pretend to love a gift that you really hated? ◯ Yes ◯ No

7. French fries: ◯ thin ◯ crinkle cut ◯ steak ◯ waffle?

8. Bagel: ◯ plain ◯ whole wheat ◯ sweet ◯ everything?

9. More about your bagel: ◯ naked ◯ cream cheese?

10. ◯ Board games ◯ Bored with games?

11. If safety weren't a problem, what animal would U have as a pet? . . . .

12. Favorite number? . . . .

13. Best advice anyone ever gave you? . . . .

14. Worst advice anyone ever gave you? . . . .

15. Ever stay up all night watching movies? ◯ Yes ◯ No

16. Ever stay up all night talking to a friend on the phone? ◯ Yes ◯ No

17. Do you order stuff on the Internet? ◯ Yes ◯ No

18. What "super sense" would U like? ◯ Hearing ◯ Sight ◯ Smell

19. What fashion item defines you? . . . .

20. Like what you are wearing right now? ◯ Yes ◯ No

1. My friends call me _____
   (name)

2. I get my music from ◯ the store ◯ online ◯ both

3. Describe your BF in 1 word _____

4. Ever want to be a d.j. on the radio? ◯ Yes ◯ No

5. If yes, what music would you play? _____

6. 🍀 Do U wear green on St. Patrick's Day? ◯ Yes ◯ No

7. Do U miss kid stuff like hunting Easter eggs? ◯ Yes ◯ No

8. How about putting your tooth under your pillow? ◯ Yes ◯ No

9. Do you know what T.T.F.N. stands 4? ◯ Yes, what?_____ ◯ No

10. How do U get a song out of your head? _____

11. What do U splurge on? _____

12. Which describes you best? ◯ Emotional ◯ Logical ◯ 50/50

13. R U ◯ extroverted ◯ introverted ◯ somewhere in the middle?

14. I prefer a ◯ picnic in the park ◯ great night out

15. Most boring sport to watch? _____

16. What celebrity your BFF would identify U with? _____

17. Ever had a premonition? ◯ Yes ◯ No

18. How would your parents describe you? _____

19. U find $50. You ◯ bank it ◯ spend it ◯ try to find its owner

20. What did you watch on TV last night? _____

Robot?
I think I'll have one to do the things I hate!

1. The name I was born with is . . . .

2. How would U spend $1000 in 1 day? . . . .

3. What have you planned that became a disaster? . . . .

4. Do U have a profile on MYSPACE? ◯ Yes ◯ No

5. Favorite book character? . . . .

6. Best band since you were born? . . . .

7. I lose track of time when I . . . .

8. Do you think you will own a robot in the future? ◯ Yes ◯ No

9. Your friends come to U when they need a ◯ pep talk ◯ reality check

10. What do U do in your spare time? . . . .

11. Do you talk 2 your pet like it's a person? ◯ Yes ◯ No

12. ◯ Spend more time dwelling on the past   ◯ Looking toward the future?

13. How long do you think civilization will last? . . . .

14. Lesson you've learned the hard way? . . . .

15. Where R U right now? . . . .

16. Who are U sitting next 2 right now? . . . .

17. How many times do you hit Snooze? . . . .

18. What do U think happens to your soul when you die? . . . .

19. ◯ Can U Yo-Yo? ◯ Yes ◯ No ◯ Who cares

20. Do U like being in the spotlight? ◯ Always ◯ Sometimes ◯ Never

1. Name on your birth certificate? _____

2. Day of the week, date, and time of your birth? _____

3. First word you said? _____

4. Most beautiful sounding language? _____

5. Feel like you're in control of your life? ◯ Yes ◯ No

6. Do U read the label on food before U buy? ◯ Yes ◯ No

7. Who do you trust with the deep stuff? _____

8. When U R mad, do U ◯ yell ◯ cry ◯ get quiet?

9. Best memory U have? _____

10. Worst memory U have? _____

11. ◯ Make quick decisions ◯ Think about it ◯ Avoid making decisions?

12. Any regrets? ◯ Yes, what?_____ ◯No

13. If U had an extra hour every day, what would U do? _____

14. Describe a typical Saturday a.m. _____

15. Ever flown in a helicopter? ◯ Yes ◯ No

16. Something most people don't know about U? _____

17. ◯ Green thumb ◯ Kill everything ◯ Never tried to grow anything?

18. ◯ Daisies ◯ Roses ◯ Other _____ ?

19. Which is worse? ◯ Paper cut ◯ Burning your tongue?

20. I'm like ◯ my mom ◯ my dad ◯ neither — I might be an alien!

1. List all the names you go by _____

2. One word to describe you? _____

3. ⚪ Unicorn ⚪ Pegasus ⚪ Dragon ⚪ Other _____

4. Ever rode on the handlebars of a bike? ⚪ Yes ⚪ No

5. What's outside your window right now? _____

6. What kind of student R U? ⚪ Great ⚪ So-so ⚪ Not-so-good

7. Who makes you laugh the hardest? _____

8. Who is your favorite superhero? _____

9. What would U like to be remembered 4? _____

10. Ever had surgery? ⚪ Yes, what kind? _____ ⚪ No

11. Favorite movie song? _____

12. What's something that amazes U? _____

13. What do U sweeten with? ⚪Pink stuff ⚪Blue stuff ⚪ Yellow stuff ⚪Real stuff

14. Read anything good lately? ⚪ Yes, what? _____ ⚪ No

15. Can you whistle a tune? ⚪ Of course ⚪ A little bit ⚪ No

16. One word to describe girls? _____

17. One word to describe boys? _____

18. Mountains: ⚪ s'mores next to the fire ⚪ climbing rocks ⚪ hiking on trails?

19. Something legal U R addicted to? _____

20. Weirdest movie you've ever seen? _____

What word do I always misspell?

Necessary

1. Last name?. . . . .

2. What do U want to B when U grow up? . . . .

3. Ever enter a competition? ⚆ Yes, what? . . . . ⚆ No

4. Did you win? ⚆ Yes, what? . . . . ⚆ Nah

5. What's your typical Sunday morning? . . . .

6. What's something U R proud of? . . . .

7. What word do U always misspell? . . . .

8. Scared of heights? ⚆ Yes ⚆ No

9. Favorite chewing gum or mint? . . . .

10. Can you use chopsticks? ⚆ Yes ⚆ No

11. What perfume/cologne do you wear? . . . .

12. ⚆ Chocolate cake with chocolate icing ⚆ Angel food cake with fruit?

13. ⚆ Pencil ⚆ Mechanical pencil ⚆ Ballpoint ⚆ Gel pen?

14. Which is worse? ⚆ Headache ⚆ Toothache ⚆ Stomachache ⚆ Backache

15. ⚆ 4.0 GPA for a year ⚆ Spending time with your crush for a year

16. What piece(s) of jewelry do U always wear? . . . .

17. What do you love about summer? . . . .

18. ⚆ Green tea ⚆ Hot tea ⚆ Iced tea ⚆ Tea cookies?

19. Ever baked a cake? ⚆ Yes ⚆ No

20. Do you believe in ⚆ fate ⚆ God ⚆ yourself?

FAVORITE FROZEN TREAT? ORANGE POPSICLE

1. First name? ◯ Yes, what is it? . . . . ◯ No

2. If U could only go to 1 concert this year, who would U see? . . . .

3. Describe the watch you're wearing. . . . .

4. Rank in order of liking: ___ Eagle ___ Horse ___ Cheetah ___ Dolphin ___ Pig

5. 😄 R U good at telling jokes? ◯ Yes ◯ No

6. Think life is ◯ fair ◯ unfair ◯ what you make it?

7. Which would U play? ◯ Damsel in distress ◯ Superhero ◯ Super villain?

8. What's your biggest question about life? . . . .

9. Ever in a school play? ◯ Yes, who/what were you? . . . . ◯ No

10. Do U listen to ◯ the words in music ◯ just the music?

11. Have a fav cartoon? ◯ Yes, what? . . . . ◯ No, don't watch anymore

12. What's cutest? ◯ Puppies ◯ Kittens ◯ Other . . . .

13. Favorite character from an animated movie? . . . .

14. Weirdest animal you've ever seen? . . . .

15. ◯ Aqua ◯ Fuchsia ◯ Mint ◯ Black ◯ Cream ◯ Violet

16. Favorite clothing brand? . . . .

17. Favorite cold beverage? . . . .

18. Your friends would describe U as ◯ sweet ◯ reliable ◯ crazy

19. Favorite frozen treat? . . . .

20. What would you like to be doing 10 years from now? . . . .

Pet trick?
My cat fetches.

1. Name _____ I wish it were _____

2. Do U feel sorry 4 the bad singers on American Idol? ◯ Yes ◯ No

3. When U talk on the phone do U: ◯ pace ◯ use hand gestures ◯ both?

4. Do you laugh when you hit your funny bone? ◯ Yes ◯ No

5. Vacation time! ◯ Big city ◯ Warm beach ◯ Another country

6. Do you like to read poetry? ◯ Yes ◯ Not really

7. R U known 4 your ◯ sense of humor ◯ good taste ◯ talent?

8. What duo R U & your bff most like? ◯ Batman & Robin ◯ Scooby & Shaggy

9. You love ◯ a little make-up ◯ a lot of make-up

10. R U ◯ Miss Adventure ◯ Miss Understood ◯ Miss Informed?

11. Favorite vegetable? _____

12. ◯ Fast food ◯ Themed restaurant ◯ Fine dining?

13. What do U do when you can't sleep? _____

14. Your dream machine is ◯ biggest SUV ◯ smallest sports car ◯ limo

15. ◯ Mac ◯ PC

16. Ever been a member of a fan club? ◯ Yes, which one? _____ ◯ No

17. Do U have a celebrity autograph? ◯ Yes, who? _____ ◯ No

18. Do U tell people when they have food stuck in their teeth? ◯ Yes ◯ No

19. Have a pet that does a cool trick? ◯ Yes, what? _____ ◯ No

20. Favorite thing hanging on your room wall? _____

1. Name? _____

2. ◯ Thick ◯ Thin ◯ Sicilian ◯ Stuffed?

3. What do U like in your H20? ◯ Lemon ◯ Lime ◯ Nothing

4. Ever been on television? ◯ Yes, why? _____ ◯ No

5. Who has it easier? ◯ Girls ◯ Boys

6. Chips: ◯ Sour cream/onion ◯ Barbeque ◯ Cheddar ◯ Plain?

7. Favorite flavor of jelly, jam or preserves?_____

8. In a long line, do U ◯ look at your watch ◯ mumble aloud ◯ wait patiently?

9. ◯ Banana ◯ Banana nut bread ◯ Banana cream pie?

10. Is it hard for you to say U R sorry? ◯ Yes ◯ No

11. ◯ Scrambled ◯ Fried ◯ Poached ◯ Hard-boiled ◯ None?

12. Most boring book you've ever read?_____

13. Favorite kind of meat?_____

14. Fav movie food? ◯ Popcorn ◯ Twizzlers ◯ Nachos ◯ Other _____?

15. What TV show would you like to star in?_____

16. What's something you love that most people hate? _____

17. Ever think U R crazy? ◯ All the time ◯ Sometimes ◯ No, everyone else is!

18. Favorite junk food?_____

19. Do you take naps? ◯ Yes ◯ No

20. ◯ Original ◯ Extra crispy ◯ Spicy?

Word I don't like?

blood.

1. First name spelled backwards? . . . .

2. Last movie U saw? . . . .

3. ○ Taco ○ Burrito ○ Enchilada ○ Fajita?

4. What's your ring tone on your cell phone? . . . .

5. What's the most popular color in your wardrobe? . . . .

6. Coolest Arctic animal? ○ Penguin ○ Polar bear ○ Harp seal ○ Killer whale

7. R U usually ○ too hot ○ too cold?

8. R U allergic to anything? ○ Yes, what? . . . . ○ No

9. Favorite CD at the moment? . . . .

10. Is it hard for U to say U R wrong? ○ Yes ○ No

11. Favorite TV actor? . . . .

12. Favorite TV actress? . . . .

13. Least favorite class in school? . . . .

14. Ever entered through a "Do Not Enter" door? ○ Yes ○ No

15. What's a word you don't like? . . . .

16. How did U meet your BF? . . . .

17. What celebrity would U not trade places with? . . . .

18. Do you study ○ in a quiet room ○ with music on ○ with TV on?

19. How many pairs of shoes do U own? ○ 10 or fewer ○ 10-20 ○ 20 plus

20. Favorite sandwich? . . . .

If U could invent something, what would it B?
time machine

1. My name is _____

2. I wish my name were _____

3. Ever been embarrassed by parents? ◯ Yes ◯ No

4. Any details 4 #3? _____

5. What famous person would you trade places with? _____

6. If you could invent something, what would it be? _____

7. How many teeth do you have? _____

8. Whiten your teeth? ◯ Yes, over-the-counter ◯ Yes, professionally ◯ No

9. How many times a day do you brush your teeth? _____

10. Rules should be ◯ followed ◯ used as guidelines ◯ broken

11. Worst fashion mistake you've ever made? _____

12. Most annoying thing about school? _____

13. Best thing about school? _____

14. Do you exercise? ◯ Yes ◯ No ◯ Sometimes

15. If yes to #14, what kind? _____

16. Most outrageous thing you've ever eaten? _____

17. ◯ Pay now, play later ◯ Play now, pay later?

18. Little kids are ◯ fun ◯ annoying?

19. Write papers ◯ in advance ◯ a few days before ◯ night before?

20. Study ◯ alone ◯ with a friend ◯ in a group?

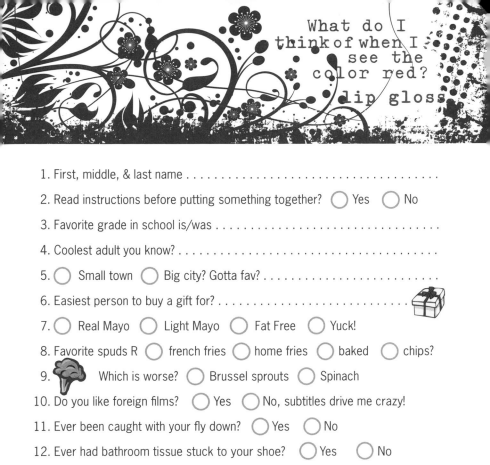

What do I think of when I see the color red? lip gloss

1. First, middle, & last name . . . .

2. Read instructions before putting something together? ◯ Yes ◯ No

3. Favorite grade in school is/was . . . .

4. Coolest adult you know? . . . .

5. ◯ Small town ◯ Big city? Gotta fav? . . . .

6. Easiest person to buy a gift for? . . . .

7. ◯ Real Mayo ◯ Light Mayo ◯ Fat Free ◯ Yuck!

8. Favorite spuds R ◯ french fries ◯ home fries ◯ baked ◯ chips?

9. Which is worse? ◯ Brussel sprouts ◯ Spinach

10. Do you like foreign films? ◯ Yes ◯ No, subtitles drive me crazy!

11. Ever been caught with your fly down? ◯ Yes ◯ No

12. Ever had bathroom tissue stuck to your shoe? ◯ Yes ◯ No

13. Ever forget to remove a price tag from your clothing? ◯ Yes ◯ No

14. What do you think of when you hear the word **orange?** . . . .

15. Who do you think of when you see the color **red?** . . . .

16. Most peaceful color? . . . .

17. Walk under ladders? ◯ Yes ◯ No

18. Open umbrellas indoors? ◯ Yes ◯ No

19. Have you ever fallen down in public? ◯ Yes ◯ No

20. Smartest person you know . . . .

1. Your name please _____

2. Last time you read a newspaper? _____

3. Last time you opened a dictionary? _____

4. Last thing you cooked? _____

5. Favorite room in the house/apartment? _____

6. Favorite decorating style? _____

7. Describe your style of dressing _____

8. R U having a ⃝ good hair day ⃝ bad hair day ⃝ so-so hair day?

9. Do you wear your friends' clothes? ⃝ Yes ⃝ No

10. Who encourages you the most? _____

11. Can you name all of Santa's reindeer? ⃝ Yes ⃝ No

12. Did you say yes? Go ahead then. _____

13. Do you like egg nog? ⃝ Yes ⃝ No

14. Favorite holiday treat? _____

15. R U squeamish? ⃝ Yes ⃝ No

16. If yes, what makes you squeamish? _____

17. R U an adventurous eater? _____

18. Camping: ⃝ tent ⃝ cabin ⃝ RV

19. Ever encounter a wild animal? ⃝ Yes, what? _____ ⃝ No

20. Favorite amusement park? _____

Best personality trait?
Loyalty

1. My initials are _____

2. Favorite kind of dog? _____

3. Your worst personality trait? _____

4. Your best personality trait? _____

5. I know a lot about _____

6. I know absolutely nothing about _____

7. Holidays are ◯ fun with my family ◯ a nightmare with my family

8. Most embarrassing moment ever was _____

9. What have U dreamed of doing, but think U can't? _____

10. Why? _____

11. Any new goals? ◯ Yes, what? _____ ◯ No

12. Ever reached a goal? ◯ Yes, what? _____ ◯ No

13. ◯ I love waking up to birds ◯ I hate birds waking me up

14. Bedtime rituals? ◯ Yes, what?_____ ◯ No

15. Morning rituals? ◯ Yes, what?_____ ◯ No

16. R U a sucker for a happy ending? ◯ Yes ◯ No

17. Who taught you how to tie your shoes? _____

18. Do you know who your Dad's hero is? ◯ Yes, who_____ ◯ No

19. How about your Mom's? ◯ Yes, who_____ ◯ No

20. Who's your hero? _____

What kind of fries do I like? It doesn't matter as long as I have ketchup.

1. My name is . . . .

2. Do you believe in magic? ◯ Yes   ◯ No

3. Worst thing U have ever eaten? . . . .

4. Movie U can watch over and over? . . . .

5. Worst show on T.V. right now? . . . .

6. Ever pretend to love a gift that you really hated? ◯ Yes ◯ No

7. French fries: ◯ thin ◯ crinkle cut ◯ steak ◯ waffle?

8. Bagel: ◯ plain ◯ whole wheat ◯ sweet ◯ everything?

9. More about your bagel: ◯ naked ◯ cream cheese?

10. ◯ Board games ◯ Bored with games?

11. If safety weren't a problem, what animal would U have as a pet? . . . .

12. Favorite number? . . . .

13. Best advice anyone ever gave you? . . . .

14. Worst advice anyone ever gave you? . . . .

15. Ever stay up all night watching movies? ◯ Yes ◯ No

16. Ever stay up all night talking to a friend on the phone? ◯ Yes ◯ No

17. Do you order stuff on the Internet? ◯ Yes ◯ No

18. What "super sense" would U like? ◯ Hearing ◯ Sight ◯ Smell

19. What fashion item defines you? . . . .

20. Like what you are wearing right now? ◯ Yes ◯ No

1. My friends call me _____
   (name)

2. I get my music from ◯ the store ◯ online ◯ both

3. Describe your BF in 1 word _____

4. Ever want to be a d.j. on the radio? ◯ Yes ◯ No

5. If yes, what music would you play? _____

6. 🍀 Do U wear green on St. Patrick's Day? ◯ Yes ◯ No

7. Do U miss kid stuff like hunting Easter eggs? ◯ Yes ◯ No

8. How about putting your tooth under your pillow? ◯ Yes ◯ No

9. Do you know what T.T.F.N. stands 4? ◯ Yes, what?_____ ◯ No

10. How do U get a song out of your head? _____

11. What do U splurge on? _____

12. Which describes you best? ◯ Emotional ◯ Logical ◯ 50/50

13. R U ◯ extroverted ◯ introverted ◯ somewhere in the middle?

14. I prefer a ◯ picnic in the park ◯ great night out

15. Most boring sport to watch? _____

16. What celebrity your BFF would identify U with? _____

17. Ever had a premonition? ◯ Yes ◯ No

18. How would your parents describe you? _____

19. U find $50. You ◯ bank it ◯ spend it ◯ try to find its owner

20. What did you watch on TV last night? _____

Robot?

I think I'll have one to do the things I hate!

1. The name I was born with is . . . .

2. How would U spend $1000 in 1 day? . . . .

3. What have you planned that became a disaster? . . . .

4. Do U have a profle on MYSPACE? ◯ Yes ◯ No

5. Favorite book character? . . . .

6. Best band since you were born? . . . .

7. I lose track of time when I . . . .

8. Do you think you will own a robot in the future? ◯ Yes ◯ No

9. Your friends come to U when they need a ◯ pep talk ◯ reality check

10. What do U do in your spare time? . . . .

11. Do you talk 2 your pet like it's a person? ◯ Yes ◯ No

12. ◯ Spend more time dwelling on the past ◯ Looking toward the future?

13. How long do you think civilization will last? . . . .

14. Lesson you've learned the hard way? . . . .

15. Where R U right now? . . . .

16. Who are U sitting next 2 right now? . . . .

17. How many times do you hit Snooze? . . . .

18. What do U think happens to your soul when you die? . . . .

19. Can U Yo-Yo? ◯ Yes ◯ No ◯ Who cares

20. Do U like being in the spotlight? ◯ Always ◯ Sometimes ◯ Never

FIRST WORD I SAID?
LUCKY (OUR DOG'S NAME)

1. Name on your birth certificate? _____

2. Day of the week, date, and time of your birth? _____

3. First word you said? _____

4. Most beautiful sounding language? _____

5. Feel like you're in control of your life? ◯ Yes ◯ No

6. Do U read the label on food before U buy? ◯ Yes ◯ No

7. Who do you trust with the deep stuff? _____

8. When U R mad, do U ◯ yell ◯ cry ◯ get quiet?

9. Best memory U have? _____

10. Worst memory U have? _____

11. ◯ Make quick decisions ◯ Think about it ◯ Avoid making decisions?

12. Any regrets? ◯ Yes, what?_____ ◯ No

13. If U had an extra hour every day, what would U do? _____

14. Describe a typical Saturday a.m. _____

15. Ever flown in a helicopter? ◯ Yes ◯ No

16. Something most people don't know about U? _____

17. ◯ Green thumb ◯ Kill everything ◯ Never tried to grow anything?

18. ◯ Daisies ◯ Roses ◯ Other _____ ?

19. Which is worse? ◯ Paper cut ◯ Burning your tongue?

20. I'm like ◯ my mom ◯ my dad ◯ neither — I might be an alien!

Something legal I'm addicted to? Diet Coke.

1. List all the names you go by _____

2. One word to describe you? _____

3. ◯ Unicorn   ◯ Pegasus   ◯ Dragon   ◯ Other _____

4. Ever rode on the handlebars of a bike?   ◯ Yes   ◯ No

5. What's outside your window right now? _____

6. What kind of student R U?   ◯ Great   ◯ So-so   ◯ Not-so-good

7. Who makes you laugh the hardest? _____

8. Who is your favorite superhero? _____

9. What would U like to be remembered 4? _____

10. Ever had surgery?   ◯ Yes, what kind? _____   ◯ No

11. Favorite movie song? _____

12. What's something that amazes U? _____

13. What do U sweeten with? ◯ Pink stuff ◯ Blue stuff ◯ Yellow stuff ◯ Real stuff

14. Read anything good lately?   ◯ Yes, what? _____   ◯ No

15. Can you whistle a tune?   ◯ Of course   ◯ A little bit   ◯ No

16. One word to describe girls? _____

17. One word to describe boys? _____

18. Mountains: ◯ s'mores next to the fire   ◯ climbing rocks   ◯ hiking on trails?

19. Something legal U R addicted to? _____

20. Weirdest movie you've ever seen? _____

What word do I always misspell?

Necessary

1. Last name?. . . . .

2. What do U want to B when U grow up? . . . .

3. Ever enter a competition? ◯ Yes, what? . . . . ◯ No

4. Did you win? ◯ Yes, what? . . . . ◯ Nah

5. What's your typical Sunday morning? . . . .

6. What's something U R proud of? . . . .

7. What word do U always misspell? . . . .

8. Scared of heights? ◯ Yes ◯ No

9. Favorite chewing gum or mint? . . . .

10. Can you use chopsticks? ◯ Yes ◯ No

11. What perfume/cologne do you wear? . . . .

12. ◯ Chocolate cake with chocolate icing ◯ Angel food cake with fruit?

13. ◯ Pencil ◯ Mechanical pencil ◯ Ballpoint ◯ Gel pen?

14. Which is worse? ◯ Headache ◯ Toothache ◯ Stomachache ◯ Backache

15. ◯ 4.0 GPA for a year ◯ Spending time with your crush for a year

16. What piece(s) of jewelry do U always wear? . . . .

17. What do you love about summer? . . . .

18. ◯ Green tea ◯ Hot tea ◯ Iced tea ◯ Tea cookies?

19. Ever baked a cake? ◯ Yes ◯ No

20. Do you believe in ◯ fate ◯ God ◯ yourself?

1. First name? ◯ Yes, what is it? . . . . ◯ No

2. If U could only go to 1 concert this year, who would U see? . . . .

3. Describe the watch you're wearing. . . . .

4. Rank in order of liking: __ Eagle __ Horse __ Cheetah __ Dolphin __ Pig

5. 😊 R U good at telling jokes? ◯ Yes ◯ No

6. Think life is ◯ fair ◯ unfair ◯ what you make it?

7. Which would U play? ◯ Damsel in distress ◯ Superhero ◯ Super villain?

8. What's your biggest question about life? . . . .

9. Ever in a school play? ◯ Yes, who/what were you? . . . . ◯ No

10. Do U listen to ◯ the words in music ◯ just the music?

11. Have a fav cartoon? ◯ Yes, what? . . . . ◯ No, don't watch anymore

12. What's cutest? ◯ Puppies ◯ Kittens ◯ Other . . . .

13. Favorite character from an animated movie? . . . .

14. Weirdest animal you've ever seen? . . . .

15. ◯ Aqua ◯ Fuchsia ◯ Mint ◯ Black ◯ Cream ◯ Violet

16. Favorite clothing brand? . . . .

17. Favorite cold beverage? 🥤 . . . .

18. Your friends would describe U as ◯ sweet ◯ reliable ◯ crazy

19. Favorite frozen treat? . . . .

20. What would you like to be doing 10 years from now? . . . .

Pet trick?
My cat fetches.

1. Name _____ I wish it were _____

2. Do U feel sorry 4 the bad singers on American Idol? ○ Yes ○ No

3. When U talk on the phone do U: ○ pace ○ use hand gestures ○ both?

4. Do you laugh when you hit your funny bone? ○ Yes ○ No

5. Vacation time! ○ Big city ○ Warm beach ○ Another country

6. Do you like to read poetry? ○ Yes ○ Not really

7. R U known 4 your ○ sense of humor ○ good taste ○ talent?

8. What duo R U & your bff most like? ○ Batman & Robin ○ Scooby & Shaggy

9. You love ○ a little make-up ○ a lot of make-up

10. R U ○ Miss Adventure ○ Miss Understood ○ Miss Informed?

11. Favorite vegetable? _____

12. ○ Fast food ○ Themed restaurant ○ Fine dining?

13. What do U do when you can't sleep? _____

14. Your dream machine is ○ biggest SUV ○ smallest sports car ○ limo

15. ○ Mac ○ PC

16. Ever been a member of a fan club? ○ Yes, which one? _____ ○ No

17. Do U have a celebrity autograph? ○ Yes, who? _____ ○ No

18. Do U tell people when they have food stuck in their teeth? ○ Yes ○ No

19. Have a pet that does a cool trick? ○ Yes, what? _____ ○ No

20. Favorite thing hanging on your room wall? _____

1. Name? _____

2. ○ Thick   ○ Thin   ○ Sicilian   ○ Stuffed?

3. What do U like in your H20?   ○ Lemon   ○ Lime   ○ Nothing

4. Ever been on television?   ○ Yes, why? _____   ○ No

5. Who has it easier?   ○ Girls   ○ Boys

6. Chips: ○ Sour cream/onion   ○ Barbeque   ○ Cheddar   ○ Plain?

7. Favorite flavor of jelly, jam or preserves?_____

8. In a long line, do U ○ look at your watch ○ mumble aloud ○ wait patiently?

9. ○ Banana   ○ Banana nut bread   ○ Banana cream pie?

10. Is it hard for you to say U R sorry? ○ Yes   ○ No

11. ○ Scrambled   ○ Fried   ○ Poached   ○ Hard-boiled   ○ None?

12. Most boring book you've ever read?_____

13. Favorite kind of meat?_____

14. Fav movie food? ○ Popcorn ○ Twizzlers ○ Nachos ○ Other _____?

15. What TV show would you like to star in?_____

16. What's something you love that most people hate? _____

17. Ever think U R crazy? ○ All the time ○ Sometimes ○ No, everyone else is!

18. Favorite junk food?_____

19. Do you take naps?   ○ Yes   ○ No

20. ○ Original   ○ Extra crispy   ○ Spicy?

Word I don't like?

blood.

1. First name spelled backwards? . . . .
2. Last movie U saw? . . . .
3. ◯ Taco   ◯ Burrito   ◯ Enchilada   ◯ Fajita?
4. What's your ring tone on your cell phone? . . . .
5. What's the most popular color in your wardrobe? . . . .
6. Coolest Arctic animal? ◯ Penguin ◯ Polar bear ◯ Harp seal ◯ Killer whale
7. R U usually ◯ too hot   ◯ too cold?
8. R U allergic to anything? ◯ Yes, what? . . . . ◯ No
9. Favorite CD at the moment? . . . .
10. Is it hard for U to say U R wrong? ◯ Yes   ◯ No
11. Favorite TV actor? . . . .
12. Favorite TV actress? . . . .
13. Least favorite class in school? . . . .
14. Ever entered through a "Do Not Enter" door? ◯ Yes ◯ No
15. What's a word you don't like? . . . .
16. How did U meet your BF? . . . .
17. What celebrity would U not trade places with? . . . .
18. Do you study ◯ in a quiet room   ◯ with music on   ◯ with TV on?
19. How many pairs of shoes do U own? ◯ 10 or fewer ◯ 10-20 ◯ 20 plus
20. Favorite sandwich? . . . .

1. My name is _____

2. I wish my name were _____

3. Ever been embarrassed by parents? ◯ Yes ◯ No

4. Any details 4 #3? _____

5. What famous person would you trade places with? _____

6. If you could invent something, what would it be? _____

7. How many teeth do you have? _____

8. Whiten your teeth? ◯ Yes, over-the-counter ◯ Yes, professionally ◯ No

9. How many times a day do you brush your teeth? _____

10. Rules should be ◯ followed ◯ used as guidelines ◯ broken

11. Worst fashion mistake you've ever made? _____

12. Most annoying thing about school? _____

13. Best thing about school? _____

14. Do you exercise? ◯ Yes ◯ No ◯ Sometimes

15. If yes to #14, what kind? _____

16. Most outrageous thing you've ever eaten? _____

17. ◯ Pay now, play later ◯ Play now, pay later?

18. Little kids are ◯ fun ◯ annoying?

19. Write papers ◯ in advance ◯ a few days before ◯ night before?

20. Study ◯ alone ◯ with a friend ◯ in a group?

What do I think of when I see the color red? lip gloss

1. First, middle, & last name . . . .

2. Read instructions before putting something together? ◯ Yes ◯ No

3. Favorite grade in school is/was . . . .

4. Coolest adult you know? . . . .

5. ◯ Small town ◯ Big city? Gotta fav? . . . .

6. Easiest person to buy a gift for? . . . . 🎁

7. ◯ Real Mayo ◯ Light Mayo ◯ Fat Free ◯ Yuck!

8. Favorite spuds R ◯ french fries ◯ home fries ◯ baked ◯ chips?

9. 🥦 Which is worse? ◯ Brussel sprouts ◯ Spinach

10. Do you like foreign films? ◯ Yes ◯ No, subtitles drive me crazy!

11. Ever been caught with your fly down? ◯ Yes ◯ No

12. Ever had bathroom tissue stuck to your shoe? ◯ Yes ◯ No

13. Ever forget to remove a price tag from your clothing? ◯ Yes ◯ No

14. What do you think of when you hear the word **orange?** . . . .

15. Who do you think of when you see the color **red?** . . . .

16. Most peaceful color? . . . .

17. Walk under ladders? ◯ Yes ◯ No

18. Open umbrellas indoors? ◯ Yes ◯ No ☂

19. Have you ever fallen down in public? ◯ Yes ◯ No

20. Smartest person you know . . . .

1. Your name please _____

2. Last time you read a newspaper? _____

3. Last time you opened a dictionary? _____

4. Last thing you cooked? _____

5. Favorite room in the house/apartment? _____

6. Favorite decorating style? _____

7. Describe your style of dressing _____

8. R U having a ◯ good hair day ◯ bad hair day ◯ so-so hair day?

9. Do you wear your friends' clothes? ◯ Yes ◯ No

10. Who encourages you the most? _____

11. Can you name all of Santa's reindeer? ◯ Yes ◯ No

12. Did you say yes? Go ahead then. _____

13. Do you like egg nog? ◯ Yes ◯ No

14. Favorite holiday treat? _____

15. R U squeamish? ◯ Yes ◯ No

16. If yes, what makes you squeamish? _____

17. R U an adventurous eater? _____

18. Camping: ◯ tent ◯ cabin ◯ RV

19. Ever encounter a wild animal? ◯ Yes, what? _____ ◯ No

20. Favorite amusement park? _____

Best personality trait?
Loyalty

1. My initials are _____

2. Favorite kind of dog? _____

3. Your worst personality trait? _____

4. Your best personality trait? _____

5. I know a lot about _____

6. I know absolutely nothing about _____

7. Holidays are ◯ fun with my family ◯ a nightmare with my family

8. Most embarrassing moment ever was _____

9. What have U dreamed of doing, but think U can't? _____

10. Why? _____

11. Any new goals? ◯ Yes, what? _____ ◯ No

12. Ever reached a goal? ◯ Yes, what? _____ ◯ No

13. ◯ I love waking up to birds ◯ I hate birds waking me up

14. Bedtime rituals? ◯ Yes, what?_____ ◯ No

15. Morning rituals? ◯ Yes, what?_____ ◯ No

16. R U a sucker for a happy ending? ◯ Yes ◯ No

17. Who taught you how to tie your shoes? _____

18. Do you know who your Dad's hero is? ◯ Yes, who_____ ◯ No

19. How about your Mom's? ◯ Yes, who_____ ◯ No

20. Who's your hero? _____

1. My name is . . . .

2. Do you believe in magic? ◯ Yes ◯ No

3. Worst thing U have ever eaten? . . . .

4. Movie U can watch over and over? . . . .

5. Worst show on T.V. right now? . . . .

6. Ever pretend to love a gift that you really hated? ◯ Yes ◯ No

7. French fries: ◯ thin ◯ crinkle cut ◯ steak ◯ waffle?

8. Bagel: ◯ plain ◯ whole wheat ◯ sweet ◯ everything?

9. More about your bagel: ◯ naked ◯ cream cheese?

10. ◯ Board games ◯ Bored with games?

11. If safety weren't a problem, what animal would U have as a pet? . . . .

12. Favorite number? . . . .

13. Best advice anyone ever gave you? . . . .

14. Worst advice anyone ever gave you? . . . .

15. Ever stay up all night watching movies? ◯ Yes ◯ No

16. Ever stay up all night talking to a friend on the phone? ◯ Yes ◯ No

17. Do you order stuff on the Internet? ◯ Yes ◯ No

18. What "super sense" would U like? ◯ Hearing ◯ Sight ◯ Smell

19. What fashion item defines you? . . . .

20. Like what you are wearing right now? ◯ Yes ◯ No

1. My friends call me _____
   (name)

2. I get my music from ◯ the store ◯ online ◯ both

3. Describe your BF in 1 word _____

4. Ever want to be a d.j. on the radio? ◯ Yes ◯ No

5. If yes, what music would you play? _____

6. Do U wear green on St. Patrick's Day? ◯ Yes ◯ No

7. Do U miss kid stuff like hunting Easter eggs? ◯ Yes ◯ No

8. How about putting your tooth under your pillow? ◯ Yes ◯ No

9. Do you know what T.T.F.N. stands 4? ◯ Yes, what?_____ ◯ No

10. How do U get a song out of your head? _____

11. What do U splurge on? _____

12. Which describes you best? ◯ Emotional ◯ Logical ◯ 50/50

13. R U ◯ extroverted ◯ introverted ◯ somewhere in the middle?

14. I prefer a ◯ picnic in the park ◯ great night out

15. Most boring sport to watch? _____

16. What celebrity your BFF would identify U with? _____

17. Ever had a premonition? ◯ Yes ◯ No

18. How would your parents describe you? _____

19. U find $50. You ◯ bank it ◯ spend it ◯ try to find its owner

20. What did you watch on TV last night? _____

Robot?
I think I'll have one to do the things I hate!

1. The name I was born with is . . . .

2. How would U spend $1000 in 1 day? . . . .

3. What have you planned that became a disaster? . . . .

4. Do U have a profle on MYSPACE? ◯ Yes ◯ No

5. Favorite book character? . . . .

6. Best band since you were born? . . . .

7. I lose track of time when I . . . .

8. Do you think you will own a robot in the future? ◯ Yes ◯ No

9. Your friends come to U when they need a ◯ pep talk ◯ reality check

10. What do U do in your spare time? . . . .

11. Do you talk 2 your pet like it's a person? ◯ Yes ◯ No

12. ◯ Spend more time dwelling on the past ◯ Looking toward the future?

13. How long do you think civilization will last? . . . .

14. Lesson you've learned the hard way? . . . .

15. Where R U right now? . . . .

16. Who are U sitting next 2 right now? . . . .

17. How many times do you hit Snooze? . . . .

18. What do U think happens to your soul when you die? . . . .

19. Can U Yo-Yo? ◯ Yes ◯ No ◯ Who cares

20. Do U like being in the spotlight? ◯ Always ◯ Sometimes ◯ Never

FIRST WORD I SAID?
LUCKY (OUR DOG'S NAME)

1. Name on your birth certificate? _____

2. Day of the week, date, and time of your birth? _____

3. First word you said? _____

4. Most beautiful sounding language? _____

5. Feel like you're in control of your life? ◯ Yes ◯ No

6. Do U read the label on food before U buy? ◯ Yes ◯ No

7. Who do you trust with the deep stuff? _____

8. When U R mad, do U ◯ yell ◯ cry ◯ get quiet?

9. Best memory U have? _____

10. Worst memory U have? _____

11. ◯ Make quick decisions ◯ Think about it ◯ Avoid making decisions?

12. Any regrets? ◯ Yes, what?_____ ◯ No

13. If U had an extra hour every day, what would U do? _____

14. Describe a typical Saturday a.m. _____

15. Ever flown in a helicopter? ◯ Yes ◯ No

16. Something most people don't know about U? _____

17. ◯ Green thumb ◯ Kill everything ◯ Never tried to grow anything?

18. ◯ Daisies ◯ Roses ◯ Other _____?

19. Which is worse? ◯ Paper cut ◯ Burning your tongue?

20. I'm like ◯ my mom ◯ my dad ◯ neither — I might be an alien!

1. List all the names you go by _____

2. One word to describe you? _____

3. ◯ Unicorn   ◯ Pegasus   ◯ Dragon   ◯ Other _____

4. Ever rode on the handlebars of a bike?   ◯ Yes   ◯ No

5. What's outside your window right now? _____

6. What kind of student R U?   ◯ Great   ◯ So-so   ◯ Not-so-good

7. Who makes you laugh the hardest? _____

8. Who is your favorite superhero? _____

9. What would U like to be remembered 4? _____

10. Ever had surgery?   ◯ Yes, what kind? _____   ◯ No

11. Favorite movie song? _____

12. What's something that amazes U? _____

13. What do U sweeten with? ◯ Pink stuff ◯ Blue stuff ◯ Yellow stuff ◯ Real stuff

14. Read anything good lately?   ◯ Yes, what? _____   ◯ No

15. Can you whistle a tune?   ◯ Of course   ◯ A little bit   ◯ No

16. One word to describe girls? _____

17. One word to describe boys? _____

18. Mountains: ◯ s'mores next to the fire ◯ climbing rocks ◯ hiking on trails?

19. Something legal U R addicted to? _____

20. Weirdest movie you've ever seen? _____

What word do I always misspell?

Necessary

1. Last name?. . . . .

2. What do U want to B when U grow up? . . . .

3. Ever enter a competition? ◯ Yes, what? . . . . ◯ No

4. Did you win? ◯ Yes, what? . . . . ◯ Nah

5. What's your typical Sunday morning? . . . .

6. What's something U R proud of? . . . .

7. What word do U always misspell? . . . .

8. Scared of heights? ◯ Yes ◯ No

9. Favorite chewing gum or mint? . . . .

10. Can you use chopsticks? ◯ Yes ◯ No

11. What perfume/cologne do you wear? . . . .

12. ◯ Chocolate cake with chocolate icing ◯ Angel food cake with fruit?

13. ◯ Pencil ◯ Mechanical pencil ◯ Ballpoint ◯ Gel pen?

14. Which is worse? ◯ Headache ◯ Toothache ◯ Stomachache ◯ Backache

15. ◯ 4.0 GPA for a year ◯ Spending time with your crush for a year

16. What piece(s) of jewelry do U always wear? . . . .

17. What do you love about summer? . . . .

18. ◯ Green tea ◯ Hot tea ◯ Iced tea ◯ Tea cookies?

19. Ever baked a cake? ◯ Yes ◯ No

20. Do you believe in ◯ fate ◯ God ◯ yourself?

1. First name? ◯ Yes, what is it? . . . . ◯ No

2. If U could only go to 1 concert this year, who would U see? . . . .

3. Describe the watch you're wearing. . . . .

4. Rank in order of liking: __ Eagle __ Horse __ Cheetah __ Dolphin __ Pig

5. ☺ R U good at telling jokes? ◯ Yes ◯ No

6. Think life is ◯ fair ◯ unfair ◯ what you make it?

7. Which would U play? ◯ Damsel in distress ◯ Superhero ◯ Super villain?

8. What's your biggest question about life? . . . .

9. Ever in a school play? ◯ Yes, who/what were you? . . . . ◯ No

10. Do U listen to ◯ the words in music ◯ just the music?

11. Have a fav cartoon? ◯ Yes, what? . . . . ◯ No, don't watch anymore

12. What's cutest? ◯ Puppies ◯ Kittens ◯ Other . . . .

13. Favorite character from an animated movie? . . . .

14. Weirdest animal you've ever seen? . . . .

15. ◯ Aqua ◯ Fuchsia ◯ Mint ◯ Black ◯ Cream ◯ Violet

16. Favorite clothing brand? . . . .

17. Favorite cold beverage? . . . .

18. Your friends would describe U as ◯ sweet ◯ reliable ◯ crazy

19. Favorite frozen treat? . . . .

20. What would you like to be doing 10 years from now? . . . .

Pet trick?
My cat fetches.

1. Name _____ I wish it were _____

2. Do U feel sorry 4 the bad singers on American Idol? ◯ Yes ◯ No

3. When U talk on the phone do U: ◯ pace ◯ use hand gestures ◯ both?

4. Do you laugh when you hit your funny bone? ◯ Yes ◯ No

5. Vacation time! ◯ Big city ◯ Warm beach ◯ Another country

6. Do you like to read poetry? ◯ Yes ◯ Not really

7. R U known 4 your ◯ sense of humor ◯ good taste ◯ talent?

8. What duo R U & your bff most like? ◯ Batman & Robin ◯ Scooby & Shaggy

9. You love ◯ a little make-up ◯ a lot of make-up

10. R U ◯ Miss Adventure ◯ Miss Understood ◯ Miss Informed?

11. Favorite vegetable? _____

12. ◯ Fast food ◯ Themed restaurant ◯ Fine dining?

13. What do U do when you can't sleep? _____

14. Your dream machine is ◯ biggest SUV ◯ smallest sports car ◯ limo

15. ◯ Mac ◯ PC

16. Ever been a member of a fan club? ◯ Yes, which one? _____ ◯ No

17. Do U have a celebrity autograph? ◯ Yes, who? _____ ◯ No

18. Do U tell people when they have food stuck in their teeth? ◯ Yes ◯ No

19. Have a pet that does a cool trick? ◯ Yes, what? _____ ◯ No

20. Favorite thing hanging on your room wall? _____

1. Name? _____

2. ◯ Thick ◯ Thin ◯ Sicilian ◯ Stuffed?

3. What do U like in your H20? ◯ Lemon ◯ Lime ◯ Nothing

4. Ever been on television? ◯ Yes, why? _____ ◯ No

5. Who has it easier? ◯ Girls ◯ Boys

6. Chips: ◯ Sour cream/onion ◯ Barbeque ◯ Cheddar ◯ Plain?

7. Favorite flavor of jelly, jam or preserves?_____

8. In a long line, do U ◯ look at your watch ◯ mumble aloud ◯ wait patiently?

9. ◯ Banana ◯ Banana nut bread ◯ Banana cream pie?

10. Is it hard for you to say U R sorry? ◯ Yes ◯ No

11. ◯ Scrambled ◯ Fried ◯ Poached ◯ Hard-boiled ◯ None?

12. Most boring book you've ever read?_____

13. Favorite kind of meat?_____

14. Fav movie food? ◯ Popcorn ◯ Twizzlers ◯ Nachos ◯ Other ____?

15. What TV show would you like to star in?_____

16. What's something you love that most people hate? _____

17. Ever think U R crazy? ◯ All the time ◯ Sometimes ◯ No, everyone else is!

18. Favorite junk food?_____

19. Do you take naps? ◯ Yes ◯ No

20. ◯ Original ◯ Extra crispy ◯ Spicy?

Word I don't like?

blood.

1. First name spelled backwards? . . . .
2. Last movie U saw? . . . .
3. ◯ Taco ◯ Burrito ◯ Enchilada ◯ Fajita?
4. What's your ring tone on your cell phone? . . . .
5. What's the most popular color in your wardrobe? . . . .
6. Coolest Arctic animal? ◯ Penguin ◯ Polar bear ◯ Harp seal ◯ Killer whale
7. R U usually ◯ too hot ◯ too cold?
8. R U allergic to anything? ◯ Yes, what? . . . . ◯ No
9. Favorite CD at the moment? . . . .
10. Is it hard for U to say U R wrong? ◯ Yes ◯ No
11. Favorite TV actor? . . . .
12. Favorite TV actress? . . . .
13. Least favorite class in school? . . . .
14. Ever entered through a "Do Not Enter" door? ◯ Yes ◯ No
15. What's a word you don't like? . . . .
16. How did U meet your BF? . . . .
17. What celebrity would U not trade places with? . . . .
18. Do you study ◯ in a quiet room ◯ with music on ◯ with TV on?
19. How many pairs of shoes do U own? ◯ 10 or fewer ◯ 10-20 ◯ 20 plus
20. Favorite sandwich? . . . .

If U could invent something,
what would it B?
time machine

1. My name is _____

2. I wish my name were _____

3. Ever been embarrassed by parents? ◯ Yes ◯ No

4. Any details 4 #3? _____

5. What famous person would you trade places with? _____

6. If you could invent something, what would it be? _____

7. How many teeth do you have? _____

8. Whiten your teeth? ◯ Yes, over-the-counter ◯ Yes, professionally ◯ No

9. How many times a day do you brush your teeth? _____

10. Rules should be ◯ followed ◯ used as guidelines ◯ broken

11. Worst fashion mistake you've ever made? _____

12. Most annoying thing about school? _____

13. Best thing about school? _____

14. Do you exercise? ◯ Yes ◯ No ◯ Sometimes

15. If yes to #14, what kind? _____

16. Most outrageous thing you've ever eaten? _____

17. ◯ Pay now, play later ◯ Play now, pay later?

18. Little kids are ◯ fun ◯ annoying?

19. Write papers ◯ in advance ◯ a few days before ◯ night before?

20. Study ◯ alone ◯ with a friend ◯ in a group?

What do I
think of when I
see the
color red?
lip gloss

1. First, middle, & last name . . . .

2. Read instructions before putting something together? ◯ Yes ◯ No

3. Favorite grade in school is/was . . . .

4. Coolest adult you know? . . . .

5. ◯ Small town ◯ Big city? Gotta fav? . . . .

6. Easiest person to buy a gift for? . . . .

7. ◯ Real Mayo ◯ Light Mayo ◯ Fat Free ◯ Yuck!

8. Favorite spuds R ◯ french fries ◯ home fries ◯ baked ◯ chips?

9. ◯ Which is worse? ◯ Brussel sprouts ◯ Spinach

10. Do you like foreign films? ◯ Yes ◯ No, subtitles drive me crazy!

11. Ever been caught with your fly down? ◯ Yes ◯ No

12. Ever had bathroom tissue stuck to your shoe? ◯ Yes ◯ No

13. Ever forget to remove a price tag from your clothing? ◯ Yes ◯ No

14. What do you think of when you hear the word **orange?** . . . .

15. Who do you think of when you see the color **red?** . . . .

16. Most peaceful color? . . . .

17. Walk under ladders? ◯ Yes ◯ No

18. Open umbrellas indoors? ◯ Yes ◯ No

19. Have you ever fallen down in public? ◯ Yes ◯ No

20. Smartest person you know . . . .

1. Your name please _____

2. Last time you read a newspaper? _____

3. Last time you opened a dictionary? _____

4. Last thing you cooked? _____

5. Favorite room in the house/apartment? _____

6. Favorite decorating style? _____

7. Describe your style of dressing _____

8. R U having a ◯ good hair day ◯ bad hair day ◯ so-so hair day?

9. Do you wear your friends' clothes? ◯ Yes ◯ No

10. Who encourages you the most? _____

11. Can you name all of Santa's reindeer? ◯ Yes ◯ No

12. Did you say yes? Go ahead then. _____

13. Do you like egg nog? ◯ Yes ◯ No

14. Favorite holiday treat? _____

15. R U squeamish? ◯ Yes ◯ No

16. If yes, what makes you squeamish? _____

17. R U an adventurous eater? _____

18. Camping: ◯ tent ◯ cabin ◯ RV

19. Ever encounter a wild animal? ◯ Yes, what? _____ ◯ No

20. Favorite amusement park? _____

Best personality trait?
Loyalty

1. My initials are _____

2. Favorite kind of dog? _____

3. Your worst personality trait? _____

4. Your best personality trait? _____

5. I know a lot about _____

6. I know absolutely nothing about _____

7. Holidays are ◯ fun with my family ◯ a nightmare with my family

8. Most embarrassing moment ever was _____

9. What have U dreamed of doing, but think U can't? _____

10. Why? _____

11. Any new goals? ◯ Yes, what? _____ ◯ No

12. Ever reached a goal? ◯ Yes, what? _____ ◯ No

13. ◯ I love waking up to birds ◯ I hate birds waking me up

14. Bedtime rituals? ◯ Yes, what? _____ ◯ No

15. Morning rituals? ◯ Yes, what? _____ ◯ No

16. R U a sucker for a happy ending? ◯ Yes ◯ No

17. Who taught you how to tie your shoes? _____

18. Do you know who your Dad's hero is? ◯ Yes, who _____ ◯ No

19. How about your Mom's? ◯ Yes, who _____ ◯ No

20. Who's your hero? _____

What kind of fries do I like?
It doesn't matter as long as I have ketchup.

★ ★ ★ ★ ★

1. My name is . . . .

2. Do you believe in magic? ◯ Yes   ◯ No

3. Worst thing U have ever eaten? . . . .

4. Movie U can watch over and over? . . . .

5. Worst show on T.V. right now? . . . .

6. Ever pretend to love a gift that you really hated? ◯ Yes   ◯ No

7. French fries: ◯ thin ◯ crinkle cut ◯ steak ◯ waffle?

8. Bagel: ◯ plain ◯ whole wheat ◯ sweet ◯ everything?

9. More about your bagel: ◯ naked   ◯ cream cheese?

10. ◯ Board games ◯ Bored with games?

11. If safety weren't a problem, what animal would U have as a pet? . . . .

12. Favorite number? . . . .

13. Best advice anyone ever gave you? . . . .

14. Worst advice anyone ever gave you? . . . .

15.   Ever stay up all night watching movies? ◯ Yes ◯ No

16. Ever stay up all night talking to a friend on the phone? ◯ Yes ◯ No

17. Do you order stuff on the Internet? ◯ Yes ◯ No

18. What "super sense" would U like? ◯ Hearing ◯ Sight ◯ Smell

19. What fashion item defines you? . . . .

20. Like what you are wearing right now? ◯ Yes ◯ No

1. My friends call me _____
   (name)

2. I get my music from ◯ the store   ◯ online   ◯ both

3. Describe your BF in 1 word _____

4. Ever want to be a d.j. on the radio?   ◯ Yes   ◯ No

5. If yes, what music would you play? _____

6. Do U wear green on St. Patrick's Day?   ◯ Yes   ◯ No

7. Do U miss kid stuff like hunting Easter eggs?   ◯ Yes   ◯ No

8. How about putting your tooth under your pillow?   ◯ Yes   ◯ No

9. Do you know what T.T.F.N. stands 4?   ◯ Yes, what?_____   ◯ No

10. How do U get a song out of your head? _____

11. What do U splurge on? _____

12. Which describes you best?   ◯ Emotional   ◯ Logical   ◯ 50/50

13. R U   ◯ extroverted   ◯ introverted   ◯ somewhere in the middle?

14. I prefer a   ◯ picnic in the park   ◯ great night out

15. Most boring sport to watch? _____

16. What celebrity your BFF would identify U with? _____

17. Ever had a premonition?   ◯ Yes   ◯ No

18. How would your parents describe you? _____

19. U find $50. You   ◯ bank it   ◯ spend it   ◯ try to find its owner

20. What did you watch on TV last night? _____

Robot?
I think I'll have one to do the things I hate!

1. The name I was born with is . . . .

2. How would U spend $1000 in 1 day? . . . .

3. What have you planned that became a disaster? . . . .

4. Do U have a profle on MYSPACE? ◯ Yes ◯ No

5. Favorite book character? . . . .

6. Best band since you were born? . . . .

7. I lose track of time when I . . . .

8. Do you think you will own a robot in the future? ◯ Yes ◯ No

9. Your friends come to U when they need a ◯ pep talk ◯ reality check

10. What do U do in your spare time? . . . .

11. Do you talk 2 your pet like it's a person? ◯ Yes ◯ No

12. ◯ Spend more time dwelling on the past ◯ Looking toward the future?

13. How long do you think civilization will last? . . . .

14. Lesson you've learned the hard way? . . . .

15. Where R U right now? . . . .

16. Who are U sitting next 2 right now? . . . .

17. How many times do you hit Snooze? . . . .

18. What do U think happens to your soul when you die? . . . .

19. ◯ Can U Yo-Yo? ◯ Yes ◯ No ◯ Who cares

20. Do U like being in the spotlight? ◯ Always ◯ Sometimes ◯ Never

FIRST WORD I SAID?
LUCKY (OUR DOG'S NAME)

1. Name on your birth certificate? _____

2. Day of the week, date, and time of your birth? _____

3. First word you said? _____

4. Most beautiful sounding language? _____

5. Feel like you're in control of your life? ◯ Yes ◯ No

6. Do U read the label on food before U buy? ◯ Yes ◯ No

7. Who do you trust with the deep stuff? _____

8. When U R mad, do U ◯ yell ◯ cry ◯ get quiet?

9. Best memory U have? _____

10. Worst memory U have? _____

11. ◯ Make quick decisions ◯ Think about it ◯ Avoid making decisions?

12. Any regrets? ◯ Yes, what?_____ ◯ No

13. If U had an extra hour every day, what would U do? _____

14. Describe a typical Saturday a.m. _____

15. Ever flown in a helicopter? ◯ Yes ◯ No

16. Something most people don't know about U? _____

17. ◯ Green thumb ◯ Kill everything ◯ Never tried to grow anything?

18. ◯ Daisies ◯ Roses ◯ Other _____?

19. Which is worse? ◯ Paper cut ◯ Burning your tongue?

20. I'm like ◯ my mom ◯ my dad ◯ neither — I might be an alien!

1. List all the names you go by _____

2. One word to describe you? _____

3. ◯ Unicorn   ◯ Pegasus   ◯ Dragon   ◯ Other _____

4. Ever rode on the handlebars of a bike? ◯ Yes   ◯ No

5. What's outside your window right now? _____

6. What kind of student R U? ◯ Great   ◯ So-so   ◯ Not-so-good

7. Who makes you laugh the hardest? _____

8. Who is your favorite superhero? _____

9. What would U like to be remembered 4? _____

10. Ever had surgery? ◯ Yes, what kind? _____   ◯ No

11. Favorite movie song? _____

12. What's something that amazes U? _____

13. What do U sweeten with? ◯ Pink stuff ◯ Blue stuff ◯ Yellow stuff ◯ Real stuff

14. Read anything good lately? ◯ Yes, what? _____   ◯ No

15. Can you whistle a tune? ◯ Of course   ◯ A little bit   ◯ No

16. One word to describe girls? _____

17. One word to describe boys? _____

18. Mountains: ◯ s'mores next to the fire ◯ climbing rocks ◯ hiking on trails?

19. Something legal U R addicted to? _____

20. Weirdest movie you've ever seen? _____

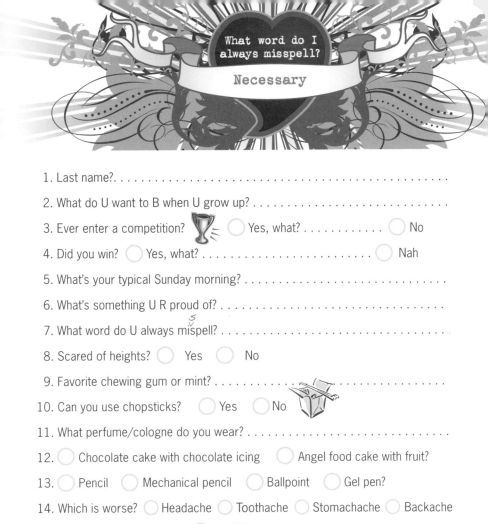

What word do I always misspell?

Necessary

1. Last name?. . . . .

2. What do U want to B when U grow up?. . . . .

3. Ever enter a competition? ◯ Yes, what?. . . . . ◯ No

4. Did you win? ◯ Yes, what?. . . . . ◯ Nah

5. What's your typical Sunday morning?. . . . .

6. What's something U R proud of?. . . . .

7. What word do U always misspell?. . . . .

8. Scared of heights? ◯ Yes ◯ No

9. Favorite chewing gum or mint?. . . . .

10. Can you use chopsticks? ◯ Yes ◯ No

11. What perfume/cologne do you wear?. . . . .

12. ◯ Chocolate cake with chocolate icing ◯ Angel food cake with fruit?

13. ◯ Pencil ◯ Mechanical pencil ◯ Ballpoint ◯ Gel pen?

14. Which is worse? ◯ Headache ◯ Toothache ◯ Stomachache ◯ Backache

15. ◯ 4.0 GPA for a year ◯ Spending time with your crush for a year

16. What piece(s) of jewelry do U always wear?. . . . .

17. What do you love about summer?. . . . .

18. ◯ Green tea ◯ Hot tea ◯ Iced tea ◯ Tea cookies?

19. Ever baked a cake? ◯ Yes ◯ No

20. Do you believe in ◯ fate ◯ God ◯ yourself?

FAVORITE
FROZEN
TREAT?

ORANGE
POPSICLE

1. First name? ◯ Yes, what is it? . . . . ◯ No

2. If U could only go to 1 concert this year, who would U see? . . . .

3. Describe the watch you're wearing. . . . .

4. Rank in order of liking: — Eagle — Horse — Cheetah — Dolphin — Pig

5. 😄 R U good at telling jokes? ◯ Yes ◯ No

6. Think life is ◯ fair ◯ unfair ◯ what you make it?

7. Which would U play? ◯ Damsel in distress ◯ Superhero ◯ Super villain?

8. What's your biggest question about life? . . . .

9. Ever in a school play? ◯ Yes, who/what were you? . . . . ◯ No

10. Do U listen to ◯ the words in music ◯ just the music?

11. Have a fav cartoon? ◯ Yes, what? . . . . ◯ No, don't watch anymore

12. What's cutest? ◯ Puppies ◯ Kittens ◯ Other . . . .

13. Favorite character from an animated movie? . . . .

14. Weirdest animal you've ever seen? . . . .

15. ◯ Aqua ◯ Fuchsia ◯ Mint ◯ Black ◯ Cream ◯ Violet

16. Favorite clothing brand? . . . .

17. Favorite cold beverage? . . . .

18. Your friends would describe U as ◯ sweet ◯ reliable ◯ crazy

19. Favorite frozen treat? . . . .

20. What would you like to be doing 10 years from now? . . . .

Pet trick?
My cat fetches.

1. Name _____ I wish it were _____

2. Do U feel sorry 4 the bad singers on American Idol? ◯ Yes ◯ No

3. When U talk on the phone do U: ◯ pace ◯ use hand gestures ◯ both?

4. Do you laugh when you hit your funny bone? ◯ Yes ◯ No

5. Vacation time! ◯ Big city ◯ Warm beach ◯ Another country

6. Do you like to read poetry? ◯ Yes ◯ Not really

7. R U known 4 your ◯ sense of humor ◯ good taste ◯ talent?

8. What duo R U & your bff most like? ◯ Batman & Robin ◯ Scooby & Shaggy

9. You love ◯ a little make-up ◯ a lot of make-up

10. R U ◯ Miss Adventure ◯ Miss Understood ◯ Miss Informed?

11. Favorite vegetable? _____

12. ◯ Fast food ◯ Themed restaurant ◯ Fine dining?

13. What do U do when you can't sleep? _____

14. Your dream machine is ◯ biggest SUV ◯ smallest sports car ◯ limo

15. ◯ Mac ◯ PC

16. Ever been a member of a fan club? ◯ Yes, which one? _____ ◯ No

17. Do U have a celebrity autograph? ◯ Yes, who? _____ ◯ No

18. Do U tell people when they have food stuck in their teeth? ◯ Yes ◯ No

19. Have a pet that does a cool trick? ◯ Yes, what? _____ ◯ No

20. Favorite thing hanging on your room wall? _____

Check out

coke-or-pepsi.com

Take more quizzes

Shop the online store for cool new stuff!

MORE

coke **OR**

pepsi?

Which direction did U choose?